Volume **12**
of fifteen volumes

PIONEERS AND PATRIOTS

CHILDCRAFT

The How and Why Library

Managing Editor, George S. Amsbary
Art Director, Gordon J. Kwiatkowski
Volume Editor, Charles M. Block
Assistant Editor, Mary Kae O'Grady
Volume Layout Artists, Clark Bruorton,
Elizabeth Schon

FIELD ENTERPRISES EDUCATIONAL CORPORATION
Merchandise Mart Plaza · Chicago 54, Illinois

Acknowledgments

The publishers of CHILDCRAFT, *The* How and Why
Library, gratefully acknowledge the courtesy of
the following publisher for permission to use a
copyrighted illustration. Full illustration acknowl-
edgments for this volume appear on page 366.

Time Inc.: photography by A. Y. Owen, page 331, courtesy *Life* Magazine, copyright 1956 by Time Inc.

Pioneers and Patriots

In this volume are forty-four unusual stories.

Read one of the stories, and you'll begin to see what is unusual about it. Like all good stories, it begins with someone in the midst of a difficult situation. Some problem confronts him; some obstacle must be overcome. Then comes the climax. Finally, we learn whether the hero of the story succeeds or fails.

Sometimes he succeeds, and sometimes he doesn't. That's the way life is, and that's the way good stories are. But thus far, although you have enjoyed reading a good story, nothing seems particularly unusual. Then you notice a brief paragraph that is separated from the end of the story—a short epilogue. Until now you thought you had been reading a story about just anyone—a fictional character. Suddenly, you discover that the hero of the story really lived. Not only that, but you find that he (or she) was a famous person—a person who has been an important pioneer or patriot. And you find that this story is not fiction (although it is written in a fictional manner), but that it really happened!

You have experienced a new dimension in storytelling. The stories in this volume (and in Volumes 11 and 13, too) are also biographical sketches of some of the great human beings who have lived on this earth. Sometimes the story takes place during the hero's greatest moment in life. But in no case are these the kinds of biographies that relate the dates, the data, and the details (see THE WORLD BOOK ENCYCLOPEDIA for excellent detailed biographies). They are biographical sketches which convey the spirit and the character of the great.

And that is not all. In addition to having gained new biographical insights, you have participated in a slice of history. Again not the history of dates and details, but the history of human compassion, human courage, human intelligence, the human spirit. To fill out the picture, a selected list of other books to read appears at the end of each story. And at the end of the volume you will find a fascinating time chart showing when each hero lived in the more than three-thousand-year span covered by this volume, and how his time of life related to the great events of all time, and to the lives of the other great human beings whose stories appear in this volume.

There are many facts in this volume. But perhaps the most important fact of all is that the great people who speak and act in these pages are simply human beings. These are stories of real people doing real things. The fact that they are also about great people perhaps only makes us realize how potentially great we all are.

These are stories—unusual stories, yes—but stories. Most of all, we hope you enjoy them.

The Editors

VOLUME

12 Pioneers and Patriots

CONTENTS

Pioneers and Patriots *(continued)*

THE MONSTER'S RIDDLE

BY S. L. BINSTOCK

One day Oedipus, a young man who lived in the city of Corinth, came to ask the oracle a question. The oracle was supposed to know the answers to everything. Oedipus wished to know what life had in store for him.

The oracle said to Oedipus, "Apollo, God of the Sun, commands that you go to the city of Thebes, for there you will find fame and fortune."

Oedipus lost no time preparing for his journey. Thebes was a long distance from Corinth, but Oedipus did not care. His heart was filled with gladness. The god, Apollo, had said that fame and fortune would be his.

He had to travel by foot. This did not cause him any worry, for he was young and strong. As he walked along the hot, dusty road, every tree seemed to wave a leafy greeting, and every bird seemed to sing of the glory which would be his in Thebes. At night he camped under the stars and lay awake for hours, staring up at the heavens and wondering what Apollo had planned for him.

On the third day of his travels when the sun was almost directly overhead in the sky, Oedipus knew that his journey was nearing an end.

I have heard that Thebes is a three-day journey from Corinth, he thought. It cannot be far. I hope that I meet another traveler so I may ask him the distance to Thebes.

Oedipus did not have long to wait for his wish to come true. The road wound up a hill, and when Oedipus reached the top of the hill, he saw not one, but several travelers—men, women, and children, and horses carrying great loads.

They do not seem to be merchants, thought Oedipus. I wonder where so many people are going.

As he approached the travelers, Oedipus could see that they were led by an old man with gray hair and a long gray beard.

"Good day to you, sir," said Oedipus. "May I ask a question of you?"

The old man raised his hand high and the procession halted.

"What is it, my son?" the old man replied.

"I am Oedipus of Corinth. I am on my way to Thebes. I would like to know how far that city is from where we now stand."

Oedipus noticed that the old man stared at him with a look of great surprise on his face. He also noticed that the other travelers, who had been near enough to hear his words, looked at him as if he were some strange creature.

"What have I said to offend you?" asked Oedipus.

The old man smiled and put his hand on Oedipus' shoulder.

"Your words do not offend us, young Oedipus, but they do surprise us. However, I think that you do not know."

"Do not know? Do not know what?" asked Oedipus.

"You do not know that you cannot enter Thebes. No one can. To try may cost you your life."

Oedipus clutched the old man's arm. "Is there some sickness in the city?" he asked.

The old man turned and pointed with his wrinkled arm. "Do you see that mountain in the distance? That is Mount Phicium. To get to Thebes one must pass over that mountain. Once Mount Phicium was a beautiful sight to the people of Thebes and to those traveling there. But now it is a dreaded sight. A monster, known as the Sphinx, now lives on the top of the mountain. The Sphinx has brought great misery to Thebes because no person has been able to enter the city since first she came."

"Then I shall fight this monster," cried Oedipus.

"You have great courage," said the old man. "But you cannot defeat her in combat. Although she has the head of a woman, she has the body of a lion, the wings of an eagle, and the tail of a serpent. There is but one way a person can pass by her and enter the city."

"How is that?" asked Oedipus.

"When she first came upon us, the monster told the people of Thebes that she would not harm anyone *leaving* the city. But she would stop those wishing to enter Thebes and ask them a riddle. If they could answer the riddle, they would pass unharmed. But if they could not supply the answer, she would kill them on the spot."

"Tell me," said Oedipus. "What is this riddle?"

"No one knows what it is," answered the old man. "All those who have heard it have perished. Alas, although many have tried to give the monster the answer to her riddle, none has succeeded. Their bones are scattered about the gates of the city. Thebes is a dying city. Food is scarce. We could not go outside the city to plant in the fields or to hunt for food, for fear that we could not get back inside the gates. No merchant can enter the city to sell us his wares. That is why we are leaving."

Suddenly, Oedipus stepped back a few paces so that he might be able to see the entire group of travelers.

"Friends!" he shouted. "Come back with me to Thebes, for tonight you will sleep in your beloved city. I, Oedipus of Corinth, have been commanded by the oracle to go to Thebes. The oracle told me that Apollo said I would find fame and fortune there. Surely, the god would not send me to Thebes if he did not have some plan. I know that he means for me to vanquish the Sphinx."

When he had said this, there was much talk among the travelers, but Oedipus could not hear their words.

The old man stepped forward. "We cannot go back with you. This is a difficult journey. If you are killed by the Sphinx, we would have to start again from the beginning. But since you are sent by Apollo, we will not go on with our journey until we learn of your fate. We will camp here, and I will send two young men with you. They can return and tell us if you have succeeded in your mission."

"So be it," replied Oedipus. "I wish to go immediately."

The old man turned to his companions and called two names. Two youths approached the spot where he and Oedipus stood. After the old man explained what was expected of them, the two youths joined Oedipus and the three young men started for Thebes.

When they had nearly reached the top of Mount Phicium, one of the young men turned to Oedipus. "We will go no farther," he said. "You will see the Sphinx when you take a few more steps. If you do defeat her as you think you will, it will be easy for you to run back and tell us. If you are determined to do this, then may the gods be with you." They shook hands, and Oedipus walked on.

Just as his companion had said, Oedipus had taken only a few steps when he reached the top of the mountain and came upon the Sphinx. She was, as the old man had told him, a horrible monster. Even the great courage of Oedipus faltered when he saw her. But remembering the words of the oracle, he walked straight toward her.

The Sphinx had been lying down, but when she saw Oedipus approaching, she raised her lion's body and her serpent's tail began twisting in the air.

"Good day to you young man," the Sphinx said in a cackling voice. "Where are you going?"

"I am going down there," answered Oedipus pointing at the city of Thebes which lay before him at the bottom of the mountain.

"Maybe you will," said the Sphinx. "And maybe you will meet your death if you do not turn around and go back."

"I shall not go back," replied Oedipus. "And I shall not die this day."

"Very well," cackled the monster. "Then I shall ask you my riddle. If you give me the correct answer to the riddle, you may pass on to Thebes. But if you fail to answer it correctly, I shall pounce on you and kill you in an instant."

"Ask your riddle, monster," said Oedipus.

"Here is the riddle," said the Sphinx.

"What has only one voice, but sometimes has four legs, sometimes two legs, and sometimes three legs, and is weakest when it has the most?"

It was a difficult riddle. Oedipus began to think very hard. As he thought, he gazed down at the city and saw that there were many people in the streets of Thebes pointing up to where he and the Sphinx stood. While he watched, more and more people came out of their homes to stare up at them.

Presently the Sphinx said, "I have given you enough time for thought. Do you have the answer to my riddle?"

Suddenly, the answer came into Oedipus' mind as if by magic.

"Yes," cried Oedipus. "I do have your answer. The answer to your riddle is 'MAN.'"

"You have not answered it all," replied the monster. "You must tell me the reasons for your answer."

"A man speaks with one voice," said Oedipus. "When he is an infant, he crawls on his hands and knees. This makes four legs. When he is a young man, he walks on two legs. When he is old, he walks with a cane. This makes three legs. He is weakest when he has the most, because he is weakest when he is an infant and crawls on four legs."

The Sphinx did not expect to hear anyone give the answer to her riddle. When she heard it, she became furious. She flapped

her wings rapidly, and her tail began to twist again. She rolled on the ground in anger until she rolled off the edge of the mountain. She was so angry that she did not think to use her wings. Thus, the Sphinx fell to her death.

The people who had been watching gave forth a cheer that shook the earth.

Oedipus ran to the spot where the two young men waited for him. He told them to return to their friends to say that they could indeed sleep in their city that night.

He then climbed down the mountain. The people of Thebes were already gathered to greet him and carry him into the city. They were so thankful to Oedipus that they made him the King of Thebes. The prophecy of the oracle had come true.

The tales of Oedipus and his many adventures come to us from the legends of ancient Greece. This story is only one of his adventures. These tales have been passed down from father to son for many centuries. Many famous writers have written about Oedipus.

No one knows whether Oedipus really lived or not. But the wonderful stories about him probably will live forever.

Some Other Books To Read

Stories of the Gods and Heroes by Sally Benson. Published by The Dial Press, Inc., New York, 1940.

The First Book of Mythology by Kathleen Elgin. Published by Franklin Watts, Inc., New York, 1955.

The Golden Treasury of Myths and Legends; Adapted From the World's Great Classics by Anne Terry White. Published by Golden Press, Inc., New York, 1959.

Adventures of the Greek Heroes by Mollie McLean and Anne Wiseman. Published by Houghton Mifflin Co., Boston, 1961.

HOW THE KING WAS TRICKED

By Virginia Robinson

"I shall not take part in your war games," the King of Ithaca shouted to his men. "No! I shall never fight again, not even in games."

The men looked at one another. Had their king gone crazy?

"I won't fight, ever again," the King bellowed. "I shall spend the rest of my life here on the island of Ithaca with my family. We shall live in peace in this great palace."

His beard twitched as he walked among his men through the palace courtyard. Suddenly, he reached down and picked up a huge stone. He hurled it through the air and sent it smashing into the courtyard wall, twenty feet away.

"I shall not fight because I am too weak, and I can barely walk," he said. Then he began to laugh.

At first, the men stood in shocked silence. And then they began to laugh, too. The men pressed forward, enjoying the joke of their King, who pretended to be so weak he could not lift a finger and yet could hurl a stone that no one else could even lift, twenty feet into a wall.

The King pushed his way through them and returned to the side of his wife, Penelope.

He turned to his men. "I say to you, have your games. Wrestle! Play hard, so you may work hard. But I shall not fight again—not even in play. I have met my match—here!"

He lifted a baby boy from the arms of his wife and held the child high. The child grabbed his father's finger. The King shouted, "I must save my strength to wrestle with my son."

The men applauded, stamped their feet, and cheered as they moved out of the courtyard and into the meadow to begin their games.

The King watched them go with a smile on his face. "Nothing will make me go to war

19

again," he repeated to Penelope who stood beside him.

Penelope looked away. "You say that!" she said, scolding him gently. "But what of your promise?"

"Yes, my promise," the King said. He thought of the day many years ago when he had promised to defend Helen, the most beautiful woman in Greece, if ever she or her husband asked for help.

But no woman was so beautiful to him as his Penelope! He put one arm around her, his other arm gently cradling his son. "Helen is safe. Her husband is a strong man and can well defend her."

"That is true," said Penelope. "But I wish you had not given your promise!"

"I shall not fight again," vowed the King. "There is nothing that will take me away from you and our child. Besides, there is the warning of the gods."

Penelope's great dark eyes took fear as if a sword were suddenly thrust to her throat. "The gods? Do you mean that the gods have spoken to you through an oracle?"

"Yes. They have said that if I should leave the island of Ithaca to go to war, I would not return for twenty years. And that is why I never want to fight again," said the King.

"No!" cried Penelope, looking away. "It is—" She looked in fear down the road.

The king glanced at the road. He saw a man running toward them as swiftly as if a fire burned at his heels. "It is—what?" he asked his wife, a harsh note in his voice.

"It is as if I hear the gods laughing when you say that," said Penelope. She shivered.

The running figure came closer.

"There is nothing to fear in Ithaca," said the King. "You see only one of our shepherds coming toward us."

"And behind him?" asked Penelope, drawing closer to her husband again. "Who travels behind the shepherd?"

The King had no answer, for he saw a traveler following the shepherd. The jaw behind his great beard tightened, and a wild light came into his eyes.

Now the sound of running feet came to their ears. They watched as the shepherd burst through the palace gate and came panting and staggering to the ground before them.

"You bring news?" asked the King through tight lips.

"What do you have to say to me? Speak!"

"My king," gasped the shepherd. "The woman Helen has been kidnapped by the Trojans. Her husband calls for your help to make ready for war. The traveler who follows behind me is coming to make you keep your promise to Helen."

The King listened to the shepherd's words. He looked at his wife and saw the look of fear on her face. He looked down at the child he held in his arms. He did not want to leave. But he had promised to defend Helen. And yet he remembered the oracle's terrible warning. Twenty years! What could he do? Was there some way he could stay with his wife and child without seeming to break his promise? Suddenly he had an idea. He turned to the shepherd.

"You bring news, eh, shepherd? And what do you have to say? Speak, shepherd, for your voice comes from far away, and I hear nothing. Speak! You cannot? You have nothing to say to me, shepherd?" The King's voice grew louder and louder as the traveler entered the gate.

"Take this child, woman." The King thrust his son at Penelope.

The child began to cry.

"Take the child!" cried the King. "It is my time for the fields. I must plow! I must plow!"

The King sprang from the steps and ran through the gates toward the meadow where the men were busy with their war games.

"I must plow!" cried the King, his great voice resounding in the distance.

He seized a wooden-handled plow and turning, he ran a deep furrow across the road and back before the astounded eyes of the traveler.

The traveler turned to Penelope. "Has the great King gone crazy? The war is lost if he cannot fight with us."

"I must plow!" cried the King, and he ran the plow through the meadow, while clumps of dirt and stones flew from his path. All the while he kept thinking, I must make them believe that I have gone crazy. A crazy man would not be expected to keep his promise.

The men had stopped their games and had joined the group in front of the palace. They stared at their king in wonder.

"I must plow," cried the King, swerving back toward the palace. He ran straight into the palace wall.

"He must be out of his mind!" cried the traveler, hiding behind a large rock. "And yet I must remember that this is a shrewd and crafty king." He looked at Penelope and the shepherd.

"He *is* out of his mind!" cried the shepherd, sinking to his knees in the road and crying as if his heart would break. "Our king is out of his mind."

"Out of his mind," said Penelope softly. She began to weep, and her tears fell on the face of her child.

The King smashed the plow into the wall again and again until he finally burst through the wall and into the palace gardens.

He ran the plow through the gardens and out of the gate, heading back toward the meadow, digging a deep furrow in the earth. Then he turned the plow and headed back to the garden, straight for the traveler.

I think my plan is working, thought the King. They seem to believe me.

But then something happened! The King saw the traveler grab the baby from Penelope's arms and place the child straight in his path.

"I do not believe he is crazy," shouted the traveler. "If I am right, he will turn the plow from the path of his child."

"No! No!" cried Penelope in terror.

My son, thought the King, my beautiful son.

He turned the plow away from the child.

The traveler again placed the child in the path of the plow. The King again turned away.

A third time, and the result was the same.

The King stopped and stood with his great head bowed.

"It is no use," he said softly. "You have tricked me. I was foolish to think that I could break my promise."

Penelope stretched out her arms to her husband and cried, "It is the will of the gods, my king. You know that as well as I do. Only evil will befall us if we go against their will."

The King came slowly back to the group in front of the palace.

"The gods say that I shall wander for twenty years," he moaned. "I shall miss the youth of my wife. I shall miss the youth of my son. It will be twenty years before I return home. But I am indeed wrong to think that I could forget my pledge of honor. I made a promise, and I shall keep it. I shall fight for as long as I am needed. It is the will of the gods."

Ulysses, the King of Ithaca in this story, was one of the heroes of ancient Greece. His many thrilling adventures are told in two poems, the *Iliad* and the *Odyssey*, written by Homer, a Greek poet.

Ulysses kept his promise and went to war. The war lasted for ten years. Finally, the Trojans were defeated and Helen was saved. On his return trip Ulysses' ship was blown off course, and it took him another ten years to find his way home. The warning of the oracle had come true. Ulysses did not return home for twenty years.

The story of Ulysses is part of the folklore of ancient Greece. No one knows whether Ulysses really lived. But the stories about him have lasted for thousands of years.

Some Other Books To Read

The Adventures of Odysseus and the Tale of Troy by Padraic Colum. Published by The Macmillan Co., New York, 1918.

The Odyssey of Homer retold by Alfred J. Church. Published by The Macmillan Co., New York, 1951.

The Great

The young Greek boy had just slumped onto his straw bed when the tent flap was lifted and his friend Marcellus entered.

"Pheidippides, I've been looking all over for you!" he cried. "Come and join the victory celebration."

"No, thanks," said Pheidippides. "I'm going to celebrate by taking a nap. I just got back from Sparta. I had to carry a message to our allies."

"Too bad you missed the battle," said Marcellus, nudging his friend. "We couldn't tell which way it would go for awhile. And you should have seen General Miltiades running around like a madman, urging us to fight harder for the glory of Greece." Marcellus laughed as he remembered the General directing the battle.

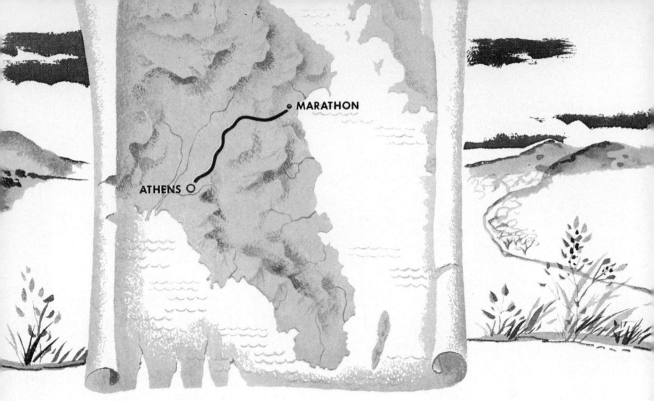

Marathon Run

By Audrey J. Geis

"You must have done a pretty good job," said Pheidippides. "I hear the Persians dropped their bows and arrows and ran for their ships."

"That was after they had lost about six thousand men," Marcellus said. "I don't think they'll be bothering the Greeks again."

Suddenly the tent flap was pulled open and a soldier poked his head in.

"What now?" asked Pheidippides sitting up.

"General Miltiades wants to see you," the soldier said. "It sounds like an emergency."

"I thought the emergencies were over when the Persians were defeated," said Marcellus.

"I don't know what it's about," the soldier replied. "But you'd better hurry."

He withdrew his head, and Pheidippides pulled himself to his feet.

"Here I go again," he sighed. He clapped Marcellus on the shoulder and said, "We'll have to celebrate later."

Then he turned and left the tent.

Miltiades was pacing back and forth when Pheidippides entered his tent.

"There you are!" shouted the General, waving his arms. "Come in, come in."

Pheidippides stood at attention as he waited for General Miltiades to stop pacing.

After a few seconds, the General stopped in front of the boy.

"Pheidippides," he said. "I have a most important mission for you. You must go to Athens at once."

"But, sir, I just returned from Sparta," the boy protested.

"Yes, yes, I know," said Miltiades. "But the Persians may be on their way to Athens to attack the city before we can get there. The people of Athens don't know about our victory, and it is possible that they will surrender the city. We must let them know that we have won here at Marathon so that they will hold out until we arrive."

Miltiades stroked his chin thoughtfully. "You are my fastest runner," he declared. "You must take the news to Athens. You are the only one I can trust to reach the city in time."

Pheidippides nodded his head. He was terribly tired. But he realized how important this mission was.

"I understand," he said quietly.

Miltiades smiled. "Good boy, I knew you would do it. Leave at once, and good luck to you!"

Pheidippides saluted and disappeared outside the tent.

The sun was hot and Pheidippides reached for his water flask. Then he remembered he had left it in his tent. He strode back, refilled the flask after taking a deep swallow, and tied it securely to his waist.

Athens was about twenty-five miles away.

Well, at least it's not as far as Sparta, he thought, as he made his way through the camp, pushing between soldiers happy with victory.

He stumbled against a tent peg and barely caught himself

from falling.

"Pheidippides, wait!"

Pheidippides turned and saw Marcellus running toward him.

"Where are you off to now?" asked Marcellus.

"I'm off to Athens," he replied. "Do you want me to give your family any message?"

"No," said Marcellus. "But I'd go slowly if I were you. You look tired."

Pheidippides shrugged, "All in a day's work." He punched his friend playfully in the arm and turned.

"See you soon," he called back.

The army was camped on the slopes of a mountain. Pheidippides decided to climb over the mountain instead of taking the longer route around it. Leaning forward, he lunged up the slopes, side-stepping rocks and weaving between the trees and bushes. At the top of the mountain he stopped to get his breath. Then he plunged down the other side to the road leading to Athens.

Here Pheidippides broke into a trot. He would take Marcellus' advice and go slowly, conserving his strength until he had covered most of the distance. Then he would draw on all his remaining energy to run full speed into the city.

After an hour, sweat was streaming down Pheidippides' forehead, but he had become accustomed to the pace he had set for himself. He was running easily with long, regular strides. He almost forgot how tired he was as he covered the dirt road with puffs of dust kicked up by his heels. He liked to run. It made him feel free and weightless.

He thought of Miltiades. The General had called him his fastest runner. And this was indeed an important mission. The fate of Athens depended on him.

I must get there before the Persians do, Pheidippides thought. Somehow I must run faster.

On he ran as mile after mile passed under his racing feet. Ten miles. Twelve. Fifteen. Could he make it? He was very tired.

Suddenly Pheidippides coughed. A film of dust clung to his skin. Dust had filled his nose and mouth until he could barely breathe. He tried to keep up the pace, but he could not stop coughing.

Gasping, he threw himself to the side of the road under an olive tree. He reached for his flask but realized that water would only make him sick now He would have to rest first. Soon he was breathing more easily. The shade sent pleasant shivers over his warm body and he began to relax. He removed the flask from his hip, rinsed out his mouth, and then took a few short swallows of the cool water.

Then Pheidippides began to think of his mission again. The entire army was with General Miltiades at Marathon. If the people of Athens thought their army had been destroyed, what would they do? There were few men left to defend the city. Would they surrender to the Persians?

Pheidippides knew he could not afford to rest any longer. The Persian ships might even now be approaching the harbor of Athens. He wiped the sweat from his face and neck. He calculated the distance he had run and decided that he had only about five more miles to go.

The boy stood up and stretched his legs. Slowly, he started off again. His legs were shaky in spite of his rest. But little by little, he increased his speed.

He was almost there. Now was the time for a burst of speed. He stretched his long legs and thrust them out, forcing his body down the road. His arms, raised slightly, pumped back and forth.

He thought that soon he would feel a rush of fresh energy, as he always did when he had been running hard. Instead, energy seemed to be seeping out of his body. With every stride, he felt as if he were moving more slowly. He pushed himself harder.

He had to reach Athens before the Persians did. He kept saying that to himself over and over again.

Ahead he could see the first farms that lay outside Athens. As he drew up to them, several men in the fields raised their heads to stare at him. He raced on.

His heart pounded against his ribs. Trees and fields passed by in a blur. Once he almost went off the road, but he threw himself in the other direction just in time. He opened his mouth wider to suck in air.

He stumbled against some children as he went through the gateway to Athens. He wanted to fall over, to collapse in the street, but his legs carried him on.

Finally, he burst into the center of the market place.

He could hear people murmuring around him and someone touched his arm. Through a blur, he saw one of the rulers of the city.

"Pheidippides, what is it?" cried the man, rushing toward him.

Pheidippides felt his legs give way. He slumped against the ruler. It was impossible to breathe, but he had to give the message. Almost in a whisper, he gasped, "Rejoice! We conquer."

Then he slid to the ground. The ruler bent down and felt the boy's heart. There was no movement. He looked up at the faces of the people crowding around.

"He is dead," the ruler said slowly. "The boy has brought us news of Marathon, and it has cost him his life. Our soldiers have defeated the Persians at Marathon. Thanks to the courage of this young boy, we know of the victory and we will not surrender our city."

"Rejoice! We conquer."
Pheidippides brings news of the victory at Marathon.

Olympic Gold Medal.
Inscription reads:
"Seventeenth Olympic Games
Rome 1960"

Pheidippides had arrived in time. The city of Athens was saved. The battle of Marathon took place about twenty-five hundred years ago. It is one of the most important battles in history. The defeat of the Persians kept them from conquering all Greece.

The heroic young messenger, Pheidippides, is remembered in the Olympic games that originated in Greece. The marathon, an endurance race of over twenty-five miles, is held in honor of his famous run from Marathon to Athens.

Some Other Books To Read

Highlights of the Olympics, from Ancient Times to the Present by John Durant. Published by Hastings House, Publishers, Inc., New York, 1961.

Life in the Ancient World by Bart Winer. Published by Random House, New York, 1961.

A GALLANT SCOTTISH KING

By Marjorie L. Knight

On a bitterly cold day in midwinter, soldiers were camped near a little town in Scotland. Their king was determined to free Scotland. He had promised to return the castles and the lands held by the English to their rightful Scottish owners. One after another, loyal Scots had come to join him. Now they were a mighty army.

But their leaders grew more worried by the hour. In a little cottage nearby, the king lay ill with a raging fever. He was not expected to live. Without the leadership of this courageous young king, whose very presence seemed to inspire the men, there did not seem to be much hope for Scotland.

This must have troubled the king. Burning with fever, he tossed about and muttered the familiar battle cries as though even in death he would fight for Scotland. Finally, he lay quite still under the heap of furs that had been piled upon him to make him sweat so that the fever would leave him.

The silence was terrifying. Outside the door the women who had been tending the king wept. They thought the end was near. The king's brother stopped pacing and held his head in his hands.

Inside the room, Douglas, the king's young page, dropped to his knees and hid his face in the furs. He did not cry. A page

does not cry, especially not the king's page. But, oh, he felt like crying. Gone were all the dreams of glory for Scotland. They would die with the king.

Then, miraculously, Douglas heard his name.

"Douglas," came a croaking whisper from the bed. "Blast you, lad! Where are you?"

Trembling, Douglas got to his feet. "I am here, my king. I have not left you."

"Then bring lights," croaked the king. "And get some of this weight off." He pushed at the furs.

"Yes, my Lord!" said Douglas. He stumbled through the darkness to the door and called to the women who now laughed for joy.

Sir Edward, the king's brother, came into the room to see for himself. Happily, they listened to the king complain that they were starving him.

There was great bustling about the cottage. The king must eat and then sleep, insisted the women, or the fever would return. Douglas must sleep, too, or they would have to nurse him.

When Douglas returned later, quite rested, he was amazed to find the king awake and waiting for him.

"Now listen well," said the king, making sure the women did not hear. "Tonight I shall sleep, but in the morning bring me my sword and armor. I shall speak to the men."

"My Lord, I would not dare—" began the frightened page. "You are not well enough."

"My enemies have spread rumors of my death," said the king. "We must stop these rumors. The men must see their king alive and on his horse. You will do as I command. I am your king."

"Yes, my Lord!" said Douglas. "I will do it."

He left to seek the advice of a good friend.

"You must do as the king commands," his friend answered thoughtfully. "For if you save him, but lose Scotland, he will never forgive you."

Early the next morning Douglas hurried to the king, carrying his armor.

The king awoke at once. "Help me to my feet," he ordered.

Douglas did his best, but it was slow work getting the king ready. The armor was heavy and the king had to stop often to catch his breath. Finally he finished.

"Now give me my great sword," said the king.

"My Lord," protested Douglas. "Please—it will be too heavy."

"Foolish lad," said the king. "I will be recognized as a sick man if I seem to lean on you. But if I lean on my great sword, they will not guess my weakness."

Douglas opened the door. When the women saw their king, they wrung their hands and cried that going out would be the death of him.

"Have my horse saddled and bring him to the door," the king ordered Douglas. Then he turned to his brother. "I am not so insane as to think I can lead the armies into battle. You must do it for me. But before the soldiers ride against the enemy, they shall see their king astride his horse waving them on to victory. When my horse comes, boost me into the saddle."

The call to arms was sounded. The men came running through the snow, buckling their sword belts as they ran. Their faces lit up with joy when they saw the king, and they shouted a mighty welcome.

The king thanked them. He told them that before long he would ride again. But for this once, his brother would lead them into battle.

"For each blow you strike, strike another for me, so we shall show our enemies that I still live," the king shouted.

The men roared their approval. The sun flashed brightly on their raised swords. And the king, swaying a little, raised his hand in a salute as the men turned to follow his brother. They would go into battle remembering their king in his royal coat with the sun gleaming on his golden crown.

When he could no longer see their banners whipping in the wind, the king, with a weary smile, permitted Douglas to help him from his horse and return him to bed.

This is the cloth pattern that stands for the Bruce family. It is called the "Bruce Tartan."

The king in this story was King Robert Bruce, who ruled Scotland hundreds of years ago.

As the legend goes, with the inspiring words of King Robert still ringing in their ears, the Scottish soldiers marched off to battle that afternoon. News came in the morning that the enemy had fled before them. The Scots went on to victory after victory. Finally, with Robert again at their head, they engaged the whole might of the English armies at Bannockburn in 1314. Here, they were able to defeat the English and drive them from the land.

From that time on, Robert Bruce was recognized even by the English to be the true King of Scotland, and all pledged their allegiance to him.

Some Other Books To Read

Robert Bruce: King of Scots by Nina Brown Baker. Published by Vanguard Press, New York, 1948.

Robert Bruce by William Croft Dickinson. Published by Thomas Nelson and Sons, New York, 1960.

The Explorer's Impossible Dream

By Audrey J. Schuster

Inside the royal palace, the Queen of Spain smoothed her skirt, folded her hands in her lap, and waited for her husband to finish speaking.

When he stopped, she said quietly, "Everything you say is true, my dear, but we have kept this poor explorer waiting for almost six years. We must give him a definite answer."

"And what do you think we should tell him?" asked the King of Spain. "Do you want me to say, 'Here is our money and here are our ships. Now take them and make fools of us'?"

"Now, now, dear," soothed the Queen. "You know that some of the wisest men in the land believe that it is possible to reach the Indies by sailing west. Why even our treasurer agrees."

"Ha! Our treasurer! A lot he knows about the sea," pouted the King. "He can't even keep the treasury filled!"

"But, dear, it wouldn't cost so much," said the Queen. "And just think how rich we would be if the man did find the Indies. All those jewels and spices—and the gold!"

The King's eyes widened for a moment. But then he frowned.

"Because of you, we set up a special committee just to study the idea," he said. "We had wise men poring over books and charts and discussing the matter for four years."

He rose and began to pace back and forth.

"They said it couldn't be done. But that wasn't good enough for you," he went on, glaring at his wife. "We appointed another committee—"

"Yes, and what did they say?" interrupted the Queen jumping up from her throne.

"Don't interrupt!" the King shouted. He lowered his voice. "All right, they gave their approval. But you know they were just telling you what you wanted to hear. It's just an impossible dream."

"And what's more, this upstart explorer has the nerve to ask to be named governor of all lands that he discovers," the King continued. "And he wants his children and his grandchildren and their children to be governors. And on top of that, he wants a share of any gold or spice that comes from these lands."

"But he hasn't found any lands yet," said the Queen.

"And I don't think he ever will!" thundered the King.

"Well, you'd better tell him that yourself," the Queen replied.

She pulled a rope at her side, and a servant entered. "Send a messenger to get the explorer," she ordered. "The King wishes to speak to him."

The explorer appeared the next day. He strode into the chamber, sweeping off his hat, and bowed to the royal couple.

"Señor explorer, how good to see you," said the Queen.

The explorer beamed and bowed again. "I am honored, your majesty."

"That's enough," snapped the King. "Let's get on with it." The King sat stiffly on his throne. "We won't keep you waiting any longer," he said. "We have decided that Spain cannot afford to pay for such a—such an uncertain venture."

The tall explorer opened his mouth to speak and stopped. He glanced at the Queen who lowered her eyes.

"But your majesty," he said. "I thought, after all this time—"

"I know, I know," said the King waving his arms. "We are sorry that we could not give you our decision sooner. But we have been very busy. We have given your plans much thought lately. We have agreed that it would be ridiculous for anyone to try to sail west in order to reach the Indies. The Indies are to the east!"

"Ridiculous?" the explorer shouted. He stepped forward angrily. Then he stepped back and waited until he was calm.

"Your majesty, your advisers are very wise men," he said finally. "But they have never sailed far out into the great ocean.

"I have been a sailor all my life," he continued. "I have studied the seas, and I have studied maps and charts."

"That is true," nodded the Queen. The King glared at her again.

"We know all that," the King said.

"Then, your majesty, you must believe that I know what I am talking about," said the explorer. "Will you not consider your duty to Spain?"

The King raised his eyebrows. "What do you mean?"

"It is not for riches alone that I would dare to sail to the Indies," continued the explorer. "I would go to spread the glory of Spain."

"But of course!" the Queen burst out.

The King stroked his beard thoughtfully. "There is no question that the Queen, or I would ever hesitate to carry forward the glory of our beloved country. Still . . ." He paused.

The explorer, his eyes shining, threw his arms wide. "This is a golden moment, your majesty. You must take this chance."

"Golden, yes," murmured the King. "And that reminds me, señor explorer, you are asking a very high price for spreading the glory of Spain."

The explorer straightened up. "I have waited many years," he said. "I have been laughed at and insulted. And all that time I knew that I was right. If I find new lands and a route to the Indies, it will not be such a high price."

"We cannot pay what you ask," the King snapped. "And we cannot promise you all those other honors and favors."

"You have heard my price," said the explorer.

"And you have heard my answer," shouted the King.

"Oh, wait," whispered the Queen.

"Be quiet," said the King. And to the explorer he added, "You are dismissed."

The explorer whirled and strode out of the room.

"Do you think we are making a mistake?" asked the Queen.

"Don't be silly. The man is simply a fortune hunter. Let's forget him." The King jumped up from his chair, settled his crown firmly on his head, and marched out.

But the Queen sat brooding. The explorer seemed like such a brave man, and so sure of himself. Was he really just a fool, as many said?

"I don't know," she said half aloud. "I just don't know."

"Your majesty!"

The Queen turned sharply toward the voice. The treasurer stood at the side door.

"What is it, Luis? Come in! Don't stand there," she ordered.

Luis glanced around to make sure no one else was in the room. Then he walked over to the Queen.

"What is the matter, Luis?" she asked again.

"I just passed the explorer outside, your majesty. He was in such a stormy mood that he didn't even wave!" exclaimed Luis. He stepped closer to the Queen. "You didn't turn him down, did you?"

The Queen frowned and tapped her long fingers on the arm of the throne. "Yes, Luis, we did. The King told him that we could not afford his wild plan."

"Oh, your majesty," moaned the treasurer. "Do you realize that may have been your last chance? I've heard that the explorer was thinking of asking the King of France for help."

"What!" cried the Queen, her eyes flashing. That would never do, she thought. Why, if the man was successful, all the glory would go to one of Spain's worst enemies!

She walked over to the window. Outside, people hurried about, busy with their daily work. She had a duty toward those people. There were other things to think about besides money. There was the glory of Spain.

She turned to Luis. "What do you really think of the explorer's plan?" she asked.

"The explorer is a bold dreamer," Luis began. "But his is a dream that is shared by many wise men. His idea makes good sense. And if anyone can find a route to the Indies, it is he. He is a good sailor. And once he sets his mind to do something, he

does not stop until it is done."

The Queen nodded and smiled. Just as I thought, she said to herself.

"And the money?" she asked.

"Your majesty, we spend more than the explorer is asking for his whole voyage when we entertain a royal visitor for one week!" the treasurer answered. "I promise you that I will raise the funds myself."

Just then a door swung open.

"The King!" hissed Luis.

"What are you two scheming?" he asked, striding toward them.

"My husband, I have wonderful news!" said the Queen. "It is all arranged."

"What is all arranged?" he asked suspiciously, as she slipped her arm through his.

"Why, the explorer's trip!"

"Now, really, my dear," said the King, pulling away from her. "I have given the explorer my answer. And I will not change it."

"Would you rather have the honor of his discoveries go to the King of France?" she asked.

"The King of France?" sputtered the King.

"Yes," she replied. "Our explorer is determined to go through with his plan. If we refuse to help him, he has no choice but to look for help elsewhere."

"Ahem," said the King, clearing his throat. He looked at the Queen and then at Luis. He paced back and forth, angrily, across the room. He walked over to the window and peered out, his hands folded behind his back. The Queen could hear him muttering to himself about the King of France. After several minutes the King stomped his foot on the floor, turned, and marched back to the Queen.

"You know, my dear," he said. "This explorer chap is a sensible fellow. Do you suppose he will still let us help him?"

"I'm sure he will," said the Queen. She turned to Luis. "Send for the explorer immediately!" she said, smiling.

Water color painting of *Columbus Taking Possession of the New World* by Johann Rugendas

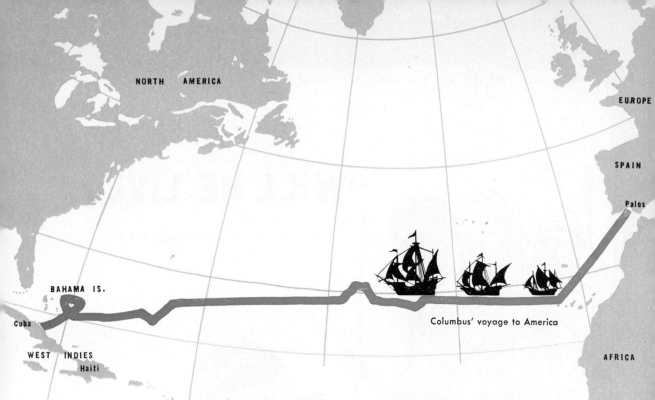

The explorer in this story was Christopher Columbus, the man who discovered America. The King and Queen of Spain were King Ferdinand and Queen Isabella.

At the time Columbus lived, sailing across the ocean to find a new land was as strange as soaring through space to another planet would be today. No one knew what dangers lurked in the ocean or what strange-looking creatures an explorer would meet in a distant land. Some people believed that the earth was flat and that a ship would fall off the edge of the earth if it sailed too far.

After more than two months at sea, Columbus found land. He thought he had reached the Indies near Japan and China, and he called the people living there "Indians." Columbus was wrong. He hadn't reached the Indies at all. And he never knew that he had discovered a new land which we know today as America.

Columbus never found out just how great his discovery was. Not until many years after his discovery did people realize that Columbus had reached a new world.

Some Other Books To Read

Voyages of Christopher Columbus by Armstrong Sperry. Published by Random House, New York, 1950.

Columbus, Finder of the New World by Ronald Syme. Published by William Morrow and Co., Inc., 1952.

The Columbus Story by Alice Dalgliesh. Published by Charles Scribner's Sons, New York, 1955.

Columbus by Ingri M. and Edgar P. D'Aulaire. Published by Doubleday and Company, Inc., New York, 1955.

47

"WILL HE LIVE?"

By Robert West Howard

The man with the tangle of reddish-brown hair lifted his left arm and shook a doll-faced copper rattle. The crowd of Indians bowed and pushed back to clear a path that led to a pile of furs. An old man, lying on the furs, groaned and held out his arms, as though begging for help.

"Come," said the man with the rattle. Three men fell into step behind him. All four men marched to the pile of furs. They knelt and stared at the red wound in the old man's back.

"It is bad," the man with the rattle finally murmured. "The arrow's point must be close to his heart. I am not a surgeon. But I must remove the arrowhead or he will die."

"If you operate and fail, Álvar, they will kill us," one of the three whispered.

"The Lord has kept us alive for a reason," Álvar said firmly. He laid down the rattle and reached into the dirty deerskin he wore around his hips. "Somehow, the Lord will see to it that at least one of us reaches the South Sea and the outposts of New Spain."

The dagger he drew from the deerskin glittered in the summer sunshine. "Estévanico!" he called to one of his companions, and held out the dagger. "Try to make them understand that this dagger must be cleansed in hot water."

Estévanico nodded. He took the dagger and holding it high above his head, he strode toward a fire that was burning in front of the largest hut in the village. He dropped the dagger into a big water jar that stood near the fire. Then he walked to the fire, reached his hands down toward the flames, drew them up in cup-shape, ran back to the water jar, and pretended to empty his cupped hands into the jar.

A warrior waved his arms and began to shout. Three women hurried around the corner of the hut. They came back carrying several round, red rocks. Estévanico smiled and nodded. The women laid the

rocks in the center of the fire. Estévanico returned to his three companions.

"They understand," he reported. "The stones are on the fire." He paused. "If help is needed, I can help," he said. "I was in the war when I was young. It was my job to hold the wounded still, while the surgeons operated."

Álvar laid an arm across Estévanico's shoulders. "I shall certainly need your help," he said. "The nearest I have ever come to surgery was when I, too, helped hold the wounded after a battle. Go now to the huts. Search for one of the needles and some of the thread these women use. These, too, must be cleansed in the hot water."

"Álvar, why do you take this chance?" one of his companions asked as Estévanico hurried away. "If you fail, we will be killed like dogs."

"The other tribes told these people that we are good medicine men," Álvar answered. "This old man is a great chief, otherwise they would not have brought him to us. If the Lord wills that I am to remove this arrow from the chief's body and heal his wound, these Indians will help us to go on toward the South Sea. Then we can find the frontiers of New Spain and tell our people about this great, unknown land."

Álvar turned and stared across the green prairie. He remembered the terrible storm when he and many other Spaniards had been shipwrecked and washed ashore. That had been several years ago. Now, he and his three companions were the only ones left alive. The rest had either starved to death or been killed by Indians.

The four men had survived only because they had decided to

make friends among the Indians. They had done what they could to care for the sick. They had taught the lame to bathe their crippled limbs and had made crutches for them. The Indians had looked upon them as good medicine men, and had let them move from tribe to tribe, in safety.

Estévanico returned from the huts. "I found them," he called to Álvar, holding a slender needle of polished deer bone and some rawhide thread in his hand. "And the stones are hot enough now to heat the water. Soon we will be ready."

Estévanico walked toward the fire. He pointed at the stones which lay in the flames and shouted.

Three Indian women ran up. Each carried two flat sticks hollowed at the ends like large spoons. They scooped a hot stone onto each stick and ran to the pottery jar full of water. They dropped the hot stones into the water, and hurried back for other stones. This was the only method the Indians knew for heating water.

Álvar walked across the village to a tree. Its wood was soft and smelled sweet. He broke off a branch as thick as his thumb and as long as his hand. Then, he trimmed away the twigs and leaves.

"The pain will be great," he explained to Estévanico. "We must persuade the chief to hold this stick between his teeth and bite into it when the knife begins to hurt. That will prevent him from biting his lips or tongue, and wounding himself."

Álvar walked back through the crowd of Indians. He knelt down beside the chief, held the stick close to his own mouth, and clenched his teeth tight. He pointed at the chief.

The chief nodded, groaned again, and clenched the stick between his teeth. Then he closed his eyes and gripped the stick
tightly with both hands.

Estévanico fished the dagger out of the hot water with two
of the wooden spoons. The Indians followed him across the
village. Some of them growled like angry dogs.

Álvar thought, If the chief dies, we four will probably be
murdered.

"We will pray," Álvar murmured, kneeling.

Estévanico laid the spoons and dagger down beside the chief
to cool. Then he, too, dropped to his knees.

Álvar made the prayer. He prayed for the skill to perform the
operation successfully.

The Indians moved in close. Álvar could feel their breath
upon his back. Two warriors pushed through to the front row,
their hands gripped tightly around their spears. But, louder than
all the mutters and shuffling, Álvar could hear the thump-thump
of his own heart as he picked up the dagger and carefully
studied the wound on the chief's back.

"Ready!" he said to Estévanico.

Quickly, Álvar cut two gashes deep in the chief's back, and
began probing for the arrowhead. He felt it, a full inch beneath
the skin. The arrow's point, he realized, was even closer to the
heart than he had suspected.

He pushed the dagger sideways against the arrowhead. The
chief's toes curled in agony. But Estévanico was holding the rest
of the chief's body motionless.

Álvar laid aside the dagger, reached his thumb and forefinger

53

into the wound, and ever so carefully began to move the arrow-head. It moved upwards. Now it was halfway out. Gently he worked the arrow upward another quarter inch.

Quickly he drew the arrowhead free, and clamped the edges of the wound together with his left hand.

"Show it to them," he whispered. "Let them see what we have done. Then pick some young leaves, heat them in the water, and bring them to me on the spoons. They will help to ease his pain."

"Will he live?" one of the other Spaniards whispered.

"It is too early to tell," Álvar answered quietly.

He threaded the needle. Then as tenderly and quickly as he could, he sewed up the wound. He was taking the last stitch when Estévanico returned with the steaming leaves. Álvar took a handful of leaves and carefully wiped the blood from the chief's back. He crumbled the rest into a soggy wad and patted them across the wound.

Estévanico pulled a fur blanket up over the chief's shoulders.

"Tomorrow, we shall know," Álvar murmured.

He and Estévanico walked back across the village to their hut. Their other two companions followed them.

Inside the hut, Álvar stretched out on a pile of skins, sighed, and fell asleep at once.

He knew nothing until he felt a hand at his shoulder and saw the grinning face of Estévanico.

"Is the chief alive?" Álvar asked.

"Alive!" Estévanico laughed. "I have threatened twice since sunrise to beat him with the spoons, because he insists on getting up, and keeps bellowing to the women for food. The bleeding has stopped."

"God be praised." Álvar bowed his head in a prayer of thanks.

"But that is not all." Estévanico pointed toward the door. "The Indians have sent the arrowhead out by a messenger to neighboring villages to report your wondrous deed. More than a hundred warriors and chiefs have come in, just to look at you. And I have found one who has promised to lead us to tribes who can show us the way to the South Sea itself."

Álvar turned slowly toward his other companions. "Now do you understand why it was the Lord's will that I perform the operation?" he asked slowly.

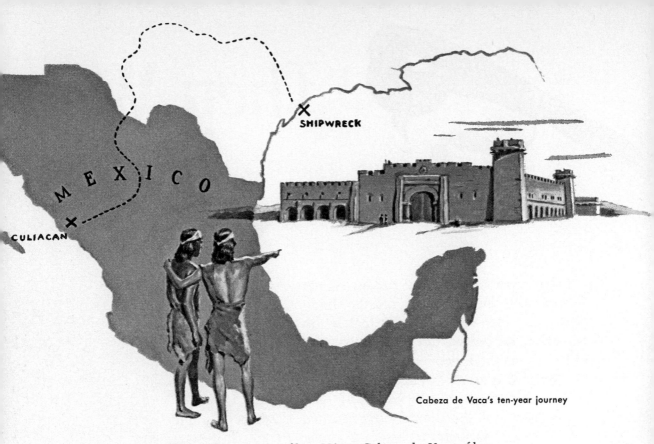

Cabeza de Vaca's ten-year journey

Álvar's full name was Álvar Núñez Cabeza de Vaca. Álvar was a little boy in Spain when Christopher Columbus discovered America. It was on a trip to the land that Columbus had discovered, that Álvar and fifty other Spaniards were shipwrecked on an island off the coast of Texas. Everyone believed that all the men in the expedition had been lost.

But ten years after the shipwreck, Álvar Núñez Cabeza de Vaca, Andrés Dorantes, Alonso del Castillo Maldonado, and Estévanico walked into the Spanish fort at Culiacan, on the Mexican coast of the Pacific Ocean, which they called the South Sea. These four men were the first Europeans to cross North America. They were the first Europeans to see the deserts, mountains, bison herds, and savage Indians of the American West. In his book, *The Shipwrecked Men*, Cabeza de Vaca told how he removed the arrow from the back of the old chief, and how this helped him to find his way to Culiacán.

Some Other Books To Read

Real Book About Explorers by Irvin Block. Published by Doubleday and Company, Inc., New York, 1952.

First Man to Cross America: The Story of Cabeza de Vaca by Ronald Syme. Published by William Morrow and Co., Inc., New York, 1961.

"They Will

By Frances Carpenter

Like a swift arrow, the Indian runner darted from the forest and into the chief's wigwam. He could hardly catch his breath as he fell on one knee before his chief, the great Powhatan.

"News! Big news, O Chief of Chiefs! I bring news of the pale-faced ones!"

The people of the Indian village rushed into the large wigwam to listen. A young girl pushed her way through the crowd. Without fear, she came close to the mighty Indian chief. She was the chief's own daughter.

The girl was anxious to hear the news that the runner brought to her father. She wanted especially to hear about the pale-faced English captain, whom she admired. "Tell your news, man!" the chief ordered.

"The pale-faced captain is our prisoner at last. Our braves are bringing him here to our village."

At these words the Indian girl gasped. She saw the look of joy that came into the fierce eyes of her father. And she was afraid.

"It is good!" said the chief. "When does the prisoner come here?"

Kill You!"

"They march with him close behind me, O Chief of Chiefs. Before the night falls, he can be put to death."

"Yes, the pale-faced one must be killed," the crowd shouted. And then the girl was even more afraid for her friend, the captain.

"We will hold a council to decide whether he will live or die," said the Powhatan.

The girl stood in the very front of the crowd that watched as the prisoner was brought into the chief's wigwam. When the captain gave her a friendly smile, tears came into her eyes. How brave he was!

The Powhatan called the leaders of the tribe together to decide what to do with the captain. Soon they reached a decision. He was to die!

There was a hush in the wigwam when the captain was thrown to the ground at the feet of the chief. Many strong hands held his head down on the flat earth. War clubs were raised, ready to beat the prisoner to death. The chief had only to say the word.

It was then that the chief's daughter

ran out of the crowd. She threw herself down at the side of the captain. With her own body, she shielded his head from the war clubs.

"Spare this man, my father!" she cried. "I claim his life for myself after our custom."

There was silence in the wigwam. But in everyone's mind there was the same thought. The chief's daughter is indeed brave. Who but she would dare speak so boldly to the chief?

The old chief looked at his daughter, and then he spoke. "Put away the war clubs! The man's life shall be spared. My daughter takes him for her brother."

So it was that the English captain was adopted into the tribe. And for a time there was peace between the Indians and the English settlers.

One year went by. And another year came. This second year was a very bad year. There was hunger and cold in the log cabins of the Englishmen. Men fell ill from lack of food. Some died. But still the English settlers stayed in the country of the Powhatan.

"At first I thought the pale-faced ones had come to us only

as visitors," the chief said one day to his daughter. "I thought they would soon go away again. Now I see that they mean to take our land for themselves. They cut our trees for their log houses. They eat our deer and our corn. It is winter. And food is hard to get. Soon we shall be hungry ourselves." The old chief shook his head.

"Now they must go back across the wide waters," he declared. "We shall starve them until they have left our lands."

The girl heard her father send out the order, "Give the pale-faced ones no corn! Give them no deer meat!"

Soon the chief's order was spread to all the Indians in the tribe. And of course, none of the Indians dared to disobey their chief.

Late one afternoon, the English captain and his men brought their small sailing ship up the river to the Powhatan's village. Behind their ship was tied a barge to carry away the corn and the deer meat which the old chief had promised them.

"But I have no corn to give you," the chief said. "There is no deer meat to spare. You say you are hungry. Then go back to your own land."

There was no friendship in the chief's hard voice. The chief's daughter stood at her father's side and was sad at heart when she heard her father speak.

"You promised me food, O Chief of Chiefs," the captain said. "We made a bargain, you and I. You wanted houses of wood. You wanted a rooster, and a hen, and copper, and beads.

"We are building your houses," he went on. "I have brought you what you asked for. I have kept my part of the bargain. Now you must keep yours. I must have food for my people."

At first the great Indian chief shook his head. But he could not go back on his word. After much talk he agreed to send baskets of corn and meat down to the ship.

The girl watched her English brother lead his men toward the river. She saw the braves bring out the baskets of food.

All seemed well now between her father and the captain. But still the girl was uneasy. And fear almost choked her when the chief began to speak to the men gathered around him.

"If we cannot starve the pale-faced ones, we shall have to kill them," he said. "Tonight we shall surprise them. We shall send them a feast in friendship. Then as they eat the feast, we will attack them."

Quietly, the chief's daughter slipped away. No one saw her

creep off into the forest. Her moccasins made no sound as she ran along the snowy trail. She had to warn the captain!

Faster and faster she ran. Like a young deer she made her way through the dark woods.

Black clouds covered the sky. She was glad there was snow on the ground. It helped her to see the dark trunks of the trees.

Twigs scratched the face of the running girl. Her flying, black hair caught on the tree branches. Her headband of precious blue beads was pulled off. But she did not turn back.

I must get there in time, she said to herself. Aloud she cried out, "Great Spirit up in the Heavens! Let me be in time!"

The darkness did not worry the brave Indian girl. Nor did the noises of the wild beasts make her afraid. An owl screeched, shrill and eerie, just over her head. A fox barked not far away. And once a deer came crashing through the trees.

But she only ran faster. She thought she could already hear the voices of the braves whom her father was sending with the feast.

At last she saw the wigwam in which the captain and his men were staying for the night. With one last great effort she rushed up to the wigwam, burst through the entrance, and stood there, panting and frightened.

"Little Sister!" the captain cried out. He could not believe what he saw.

The girl was trembling. Her breath came fast. She could scarcely speak.

"O my brother, go quickly! Go away now! The chief will kill you and your men tonight."

"Come, warm yourself, my dear child." The Englishman tried to draw the girl closer to the fire.

"There is no time," she cried. "Already the braves are on their way. They are bringing a feast for you. But it is a trick. While you eat, they will steal your thundersticks and your long knives. Then they will kill you with their war clubs."

"It shall not happen now, my dear sister. You have saved my life a second time. You have warned us in time. We shall be on guard. Our thundersticks will be ready.

Pocahontas, the young Indian girl in this story, not only saved the lives of the captain, whose name was John Smith, and his men, but, in doing so, she also saved the first English settlement in America.

This story took place long before the United States became a nation. The land of the Powhatan was the part of America we know today as Virginia.

Captain John Smith later was wounded in a gunpowder accident and sailed to England, where he recovered. Then he returned to America to explore and settle other colonies.

Pocahontas married an Englishman, John Rolfe, and went to live with him in England. She became ill and died in England at the age of twenty-two.

Ætatis suæ 21. Aº.1616.

A painting of Pocahontas

Pocahontas had played an important part in the founding of America.

Frances Carpenter, the author of this story, has written a book about Pocahontas called *Pocahontas and Her World*, published by Alfred A. Knopf, Inc., New York.

Some Other Books To Read

Pocahontas by Ingri M. and Edgar P. d'Aulaire. Published by Doubleday and Company, Inc., New York, 1946.

Pocahontas and Captain John Smith; the Story of the Virginia Colony by Marie A. Lawson. Published by Random House, New York, 1950.

CHASED BY
MOHAWK WARRIORS!

By William F. Keefe

It was early morning. A young Indian warrior came out of his lodge in the Mohawk village. He wore only moccasins and deerskin breeches. In his hand, he carried a hatchet. A knife hung from his belt.

"Orimha!" called one of the women. "Where are you going?"

The young warrior stopped. "To cut wood, mother," he answered.

The woman smiled, and Orimha walked toward the forest. But he was not thinking of his work. Today, I will return to my own people, he thought. He whispered his real name, his French name, Pierre. But the French word sounded strange. He had lived with the Mohawks for nearly two years.

Walking to the edge of the forest, he started cutting some branches. No one must know he was running away. Little by little, he moved into the thick forest.

After a while Orimha looked back. He was deep in the forest. He could no longer see the lodges or the women. He could no longer see the smoke rising from the fires.

Orimha dropped the sticks and the hatchet he was carrying and began to run. He had been well trained by the Mohawks. He could run as long and as fast as any Indian.

The sun rose higher, but the day was cool. Brambles and thorns tore at Orimha's bare shoulders and chest. Branches cut him. But he kept on. Many miles ahead was the village of Fort Orange. That was where he would be safe.

Once before Orimha had tried to escape from the Mohawks. But he had been caught.

This time, if the Mohawk warriors caught him, they would probably kill him. The Mohawks were at war with the French. The Mohawk chief had not returned from the battles. He had been gone for many weeks. If the old chief had been killed by the French, there was no chance that Orimha would be spared. He would be killed because his people had killed the chief.

All through the day he ran across glades and over hills. He was far from the Mohawk village now. But he would not be safe until he reached Fort Orange.

Night fell. Orimha knew a trail that led to Fort Orange. But he was afraid that he would meet some of the Mohawks if he followed the trail. He couldn't take the chance of being captured again. So he ran through a part of the forest where there were no paths.

Rabbits and other small creatures dashed away as the youth passed. Orimha splashed and swam across rivers and creeks. The cold water took his breath away. His feet broke the thin ice that had formed along the banks of the rivers.

Dawn made the sky bright at last. Orimha began to feel weak. He had been running a whole day and a night. He had not eaten since he had left the Indian village. He wanted to lie down, to sleep. He needed food. But he couldn't stop. The warriors were probably out looking for him already. And they would know that he was heading for Fort Orange.

Everywhere he looked in the forest, he seemed to see the faces of the warriors! He thought he saw them peering through the bushes and trees. But he ran on.

Again it was afternoon, and the sun began to settle slowly in the western sky. As the shadows of afternoon grew long, Orimha saw smoke. The smoke was coming from the chimney of a small cabin.

Orimha stopped. Moving from bush to bush, he crept closer to the cabin. A settler was cutting firewood nearby. When Orimha was very close, he called out in a friendly way. "I greet you," he said in the language spoken by the Mohawks.

At once the settler came toward him. "Let us be friends," Orimha said.

The settler smiled. He took Orimha into his cabin, and his wife fed the young boy. For the first time in many hours Orimha ate.

The settler agreed to take a message to Fort Orange. This was Orimha's best chance. The Mohawks wouldn't stop the settler. And now Orimha could rest in the safety of the settler's cabin until help came from the fort.

Orimha relaxed on a cot. He was very tired after his long journey, and soon he was sound asleep.

Suddenly he was awakened by someone shaking him. It was the settler's wife. "Mohawk warriors!" she cried. "They are coming this way."

Orimha rushed to a window. He saw a searching party of Mohawk warriors coming toward the cabin. It was too late to get away.

"Quickly!" the settler's wife urged. "Follow me!"

She led him to a corner of the room and hid him under a pile of sacks in the corner.

He heard voices outside the cabin. They must be searching for him!

They were coming closer!

Orimha held his breath and remained perfectly still. If the Indians were to find him, they would kill both him and the settler's wife.

After a long agonizing moment, the voices moved away. Then they were gone.

At last the settler's wife said, "It is safe now!"

Orimha thanked her and went back to the cot. But he was wide awake now. He couldn't sleep. He lay there resting, waiting for the settler to return.

Suddenly, he heard voices from outside. He rushed to the window and looked out. It was too dark. All he could see were four shadowy figures walking toward the cabin. It must be the warriors returning. He thought, this time they will find me.

He hurried back to the corner of the room, and buried himself under the sacks once more.

He heard voices in the cabin. He heard footsteps on the cabin floor. They came straight toward him.

Then someone began pulling the sacks from the pile under which he was hidden.

I am caught, he thought.

Orimha leaped from under the sacks, his knife ready. He would not be captured without a fight. He lunged toward the figure who stood before him. Then he stopped short. It was the settler! Behind him were three men from the fort. They had come to take Orimha back with them.

Orimha had escaped at last.

The real name of Orimha, the young boy in the story, was Pierre Esprit Radisson. He became a famous French explorer and fur trader.

This story took place over three hundred years ago in what is now New York State. Pierre Radisson was born in France. He came to Canada at the age of sixteen and was soon captured by the Indians. After his escape, Pierre explored the North American continent. He is believed to be the first white man to reach the Mississippi River and to explore the great northwest of North America.

In spite of his troubles with the Indians, Pierre never forgot the kindness of his Indian parents. Writing about his travels years later, he said, "I loved those people well."

Some Other Books To Read

Bay of the North by Ronald Syme. Published by William Morrow and Co., Inc., New York, 1950.

Captured by the Mohawks by Sterling North. Published by Houghton Mifflin Co., Boston, 1960.

Orimha of the Mohawks; The Story of Pierre Esprit Radisson Among the Indians by Charles Norman. Published by The Macmillan Co., New York, 1961.

THE EYES THAT GLEAMED

By Jo-Anne Friedman Wolfson

When I was young, I never cared much for girls. I was happiest when I went by myself and hunted, or walked through the forest, looking for new trails. Girls were always giggling and carrying on. No, sir, they weren't for me. To tell you the truth, I was kind of scared of them.

The only girl I liked at all was my sister Mary. She was sensible, not silly like other girls. But wouldn't you know it, she went and fell in love. And right away she turned into a silly, lovesick, giggling girl, just like the rest of them.

Well, I was pretty disgusted. But everything turned out all right once she got married. Soon after the wedding, Mary was her old sensible self again.

But I sure learned a lesson. I told myself, Daniel, the day will never come when you get lovesick. There's no woman who could make you act like that.

I made up my mind that I would spend my time hunting and walking through the forest. You wouldn't catch me falling in love. Not me!

IN THE DARK

Well, not long after that, I was out with a friend of mine, a boy about my age. We had been hunting all day. When it grew dark, we were still quite a way from home. But instead of camping out, we decided to hunt our way back.

We lit a fire in a big pan and held the pan in front of us as we walked along. If a deer were nearby, it would come out to see what the light was. Because an animal's eyes gleam at night, we easily could spot a deer's eyes and aim to shoot right between the eyes. Meanwhile, the firelight would dazzle the animal so that it couldn't see us.

Well, we were going along, "fire-hunting" as I described, and pretty soon I spotted a pair of eyes. While my friend held the pan, I lifted my rifle to take aim. But something was wrong. Those gleaming eyes looked blue to me. And I knew that a deer doesn't have blue eyes.

I hesitated for an instant. And in that instant the eyes disappeared. We could hear whatever it was crashing away through the brush.

We chased right after it. It had a good head start because we had to put out the fire before we ran off. But we kept following

the noise. After running a half mile or so, we came to a clearing. In the moonlight, we could see a cabin. Even in the excitement of the chase, I recognized the place and suddenly turned very shy. We were right in front of the house where Rebecca Bryan lived. She was the prettiest girl I had ever seen. But I kept telling myself that she was just another silly girl.

"Let's stop and ask Mr. Bryan about this," my friend suggested. "If that animal led us right here, it might be his pet deer or something."

I knew that people often kept deer as pets, so I agreed to go up to the cabin, even though the thought of seeing Mr. Bryan's daughter made me nervous.

We knocked, and Mr. Bryan asked us to come right in. Before we even got inside, the back door of the cabin burst open and Rebecca dashed in.

"Father, Father," she cried, and ran sobbing into his arms. Her dress was torn and dirty, and her arms and legs were cut and scratched. "The most terrible thing happened," she finally managed to say through her tears.

"I was coming home through the forest and I thought I saw a

light. Then I saw eyes staring at me. I'm sure they were a *panther's* eyes. I ran as fast as I could, and that animal chased me all the way."

By the time we got the whole story straightened out, Rebecca and I were talking and laughing together. And I guess I giggled just as much as she did. We had some cake and hot milk, and then my friend and I left.

On the way home a strange feeling came over me. Suddenly I didn't think it was so silly to be in love.

Before I could stop myself, I turned to my friend and said, "I think I'm going to marry that girl."

My friend just kept walking. After a while he said, "Well, Daniel, then it's a mighty good thing you didn't shoot her."

And that was all he said.

The boy named Daniel in this story was Daniel Boone, one of the heroes of early American history. Daniel did marry Mr. Bryan's daughter, Rebecca. And this is a story many people tell about how they met.

Many stories are told about Daniel Boone. Some are true and some are legends. The true stories tell us that in 1769 he led a group of pioneers from North Carolina, over the Allegheny Mountains, and into wild, unsettled Kentucky. The area in which they settled was named Boonesborough.

Boone showed the way west to millions of Americans. Daniel Boone had many exciting adventures. Several times he was captured by Indians, but he always managed to escape. The original trail he took from North Carolina to Kentucky is lined with markers as a tribute to Daniel Boone.

One of the legends tells us that Daniel Boone died at the age of eighty-six from eating too many sweet potatoes.

Powder Horn

Water Flask

Some Other Books To Read

Daniel Boone by James Daugherty. Published by The Viking Press, Inc., New York, 1939.

Daniel Boone by Esther Averill. Published by Harper & Brothers, New York, 1945.

Holding the Fort with Daniel Boone by Enid LaMonte Meadowcroft. Published by Thomas Y. Crowell Company, New York, 1958.

On Indian Trails with Daniel Boone by Enid LaMonte Meadowcroft. Published by Thomas Y. Crowell Company, New York, 1947.

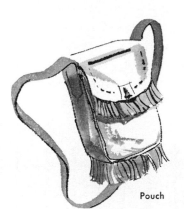

Pouch

Knife

Coonskin Cap

THE RIDE THAT

A door opened and a man slipped quietly out into the dark streets of Boston. He did not notice that his dog, Spot, had come out behind him and was following him.

The streets were filled with red-coated British soldiers. There were sounds of shouted orders and the clank of muskets. In the confusion, none of the soldiers stopped the man who walked with a dog at his heels. He made his way safely through town toward the water front to the house of his friend, Joshua.

"Joshua," he said when his friend greeted him at the door. "I need your help. The British soldiers are getting ready to attack. They're all over town already. I've warned our friends across the river to be ready.

MADE HISTORY

By Clare Thorne

But I must get word to Sam Adams and John Hancock who are hiding in Lexington."

Joshua whistled softly in surprise. "Paul," he said, "If Adams and Hancock are captured by the British, they will be sent back to England and hanged as traitors."

Paul replied, "That's right. You've got to row me across the river. I'll get a horse there and ride to Lexington to warn them."

"I'll row you across," said Joshua. "But we'd better hurry before the moon rises. There is a British ship blocking the river, and if they see us, we'll be done for."

"Let's be quick then! The moon will be up soon."

"I'll get some flannel to wrap the

79

oarlocks so they won't creak," Joshua said. "Wait for me by the boat. And you'd better take off your spurs. They might clink and arouse suspicion."

"My spurs!" Paul exclaimed. "I've forgotten them." How could he ride without his spurs when life and death would hang on his ability to get away from anyone who tried to stop him? And he would be riding a strange horse, too! He couldn't take the risk. But how could he get his spurs? It was too late to go back to the house for them. And he might not be able to get through Boston without being stopped this time. As he stood there, frowning, two little paws pushed against his knee.

"Spot! What are you doing here?" he asked. Suddenly, Paul had an idea. Spot could run faster than a man could walk. And he could get past the soldiers with no trouble. Paul scribbled a note, tied it to Spot's collar, and spoke to the little dog.

"Go straight home, Spot. Give the family this message. And come right back here with my spurs. Mind now! No stopping along the way."

The little messenger wagged his tail and was gone.

By the time Joshua had the boat ready, Spot was back. And he had done his errand. The spurs were tied securely, one to each side of his collar. Paul untied the spurs and sent Spot home again, this time to stay.

The small rowboat moved silently over the water. Paul and Joshua held their breath as the boat eased past the great black hull of the British ship. They saw the cannons that could blow the rowboat to matchsticks. They knew that the British captain had orders not to let any boat cross the river.

The moon was rising, but it was too late to do any harm. As the first long beams made streaks across the water, they reached the other side of the river without being seen.

Minutes later Paul was saddling a horse that had been given to him by one of his friends.

"It's eleven o'clock now," Paul said. "I ought to be in Lexington by midnight if this horse is as good as you say it is!"

He mounted the horse, waved good-by, and was off.

Paul rode faster and faster as he and the small strong horse became used to each other. Each time he passed a farmhouse or a village he shouted the warning, "The Regulars are out! The British are coming!"

In these houses, muskets would be pulled from under mattresses, powder horns and shot pouches filled, and horses saddled in the barn. Soon there would be dozens, perhaps hundreds of men on their way to Lexington.

Paul rode at full speed into the village of Medford. There were many people to warn here. Paul raced through the town shouting to wake the people, "The Regulars are out! The British are coming!"

Without stopping, he left Medford and continued up the road.

Now he was only a mile from the outskirts of Lexington. He would ride straight to the place where Adams and Hancock were hiding. He would warn them and go on to warn the people of Concord . . .

Suddenly, Paul saw two British officers, mounted and waiting in the shadow of an oak tree beside the road. He was so close he could see the pistols in their holsters.

They had already spotted him. One of the officers was turning his horse toward the oncoming rider. The other was starting the other way, to be ready to trap Paul if he escaped the first officer.

Paul moved the reins across his horse's neck.

"Don't fail us now!" he whispered.

The horse turned without slowing, jumped a low stone fence, and raced out across the pasture on the other side. Paul bent low over its neck like an Indian, expecting at any moment to hear the sound of a pistol shot at his back.

Behind him the heavy British horses were getting off to a slow start. The first had just leaped the fence and was starting up the slope of the pasture. Paul spurred his horse up over the top of the rise and started down the other side. Ahead he could see a small woodland where he could lose the officers, if only he could reach it.

He had a hundred yards start—perhaps a little more than that now. But it was not enough for safety.

He swerved his horse just in time to avoid a puddle of clay at the foot of the hill. He almost hadn't seen it! The soft clay would have slowed him down enough for the British officers to catch up with him.

This was his chance to escape! If only the British soldiers wouldn't notice the puddle . . .

As he rode toward the woods, he could hear the thunder of heavy hoofs as the first of the officers started down the slope.

Paul looked back over his shoulder. Yes! The red-coated officer was riding straight for the clay! A moment later the British horse was floundering in the clay puddle.

Paul chuckled into his horse's ear as they rode into the safety of the woods.

Minutes later he was in Lexington, reining his horse in front of the place where Adams and Hancock were hiding.

As he ran toward the door, two men, with muskets raised, stopped him.

"Halt!" they ordered.

"I must see Sam Adams and John Hancock!" Paul cried out.

The men said nothing.

Paul became alarmed. Was something wrong? Had Adams and Hancock been captured by the British? Had he failed in his mission? Who were these men who stood in his way? Then he realized why the men had not answered him. This hiding place had been a carefully guarded secret. For all these men knew, Paul could be a British spy. The men would not admit that Adams and Hancock were inside.

Quickly, Paul told them his name. Upon hearing it, the guards relaxed and lowered their muskets. They knew he was a friend.

"Warn Adams and Hancock!" Paul shouted. "The Regulars are out! The British are coming!"

At once the two men rushed inside with the message. Paul's mission had been successful. Adams and Hancock were warned.

But Paul was gone already. He was riding toward Concord— riding to rouse the men who would, tomorrow morning, fire the shots that would be "heard around the world!" He was riding to wake a new nation to life!

Paul Revere

The gallant rider in this story was Paul Revere, one of America's first patriots. Paul Revere's ride has become an American legend. Henry Wadsworth Longfellow wrote a poem about it called, "The Midnight Ride of Paul Revere."

His ride took place the night before the British attacked to start the Revolutionary War. But the Americans were prepared, thanks to Paul Revere.

This ride was not the only contribution Paul made to his country. He also took part in the famous Boston Tea Party in 1773. He was a lieutenant colonel in the Revolutionary Army during the war. When he was not serving his country, Paul was a silversmith.

In spite of all the things Paul Revere did for his country, he is best remembered for an event that lasted for perhaps a single hour on the night of April 18, 1775—his famous ride from Boston to Lexington, Massachusetts.

Some Other Books To Read

America's Paul Revere by Esther Forbes. Published by Houghton Mifflin Co., Boston, 1946.

Paul Revere and the Minute Men by Dorothy Canfield Fisher. Published by Random House, New York, 1950.

A TRICK THAT WORKED

By Margaret W. Gossett

"Sail ho!" cried the lookout of the *Providence* from his post near the top of the mast.

"What does she look like?" Captain Paul bellowed from the deck.

"Full rigged. Big sails. She looks like an English warship," the lookout yelled back.

Captain Paul's first thought was for the unarmed ammunition ship that the *Providence* was guarding. The ammunition ship was loaded with guns that were desperately needed for the defense of New York. If the guns were captured, General George Washington might lose the city.

Swinging swiftly up the ropes to the lookout post, Captain Paul had his spyglass out, ready to get a closer look at the enemy ship. There she was, one of the heavy English warships that had been raiding towns along the coast of the new American colonies.

With her sails spread and filled with wind, the huge English ship bore down on the smaller *Providence*. Would the small American ship be able to escape capture by this great giant of the seas?

The *Providence* was a light, fast ship. Her crew could turn her swiftly and come about in any wind. The English ship carried thirty-two guns and had a thick oaken hull. But she was heavy and slow in the water.

Yes, we could escape, thought Captain Paul. But the ammunition ship cannot.

Yet, if the *Providence* stood by to guard the ammunition ship, they both might be sunk. Captain Paul knew he had to find a way to save the guns, whatever the cost to his own ship!

Captain Paul passed the order, "All hands on deck!"

When the crew was assembled, he had them raise more sails. The *Providence* raced ahead with the added sails. But the ammunition ship still plodded along.

And then Captain Paul gave a sudden order to the slow ammunition ship, "Head due west." This was the direction of her port in New York.

Turning her sails to the wind the best she could, the ammunition ship pulled away from the speedy *Providence*. Some of the crew on the *Providence* began to wonder if they were going to abandon the ammunition ship with her precious cargo of guns.

But those who had sailed with Captain Paul before understood his courage and his skill. They knew he must have a plan to trick the enemy.

His next order proved that he did. Quickly, the crew brought the *Providence* about and turned into the wind. They headed directly for the huge English warship! Over their shoulders, the crew could see the ammunition ship plodding away to the west.

Now came the test. Would the English face their ship or go after the ammunition ship? Captain Paul counted on his knowledge of the English navy. He knew that it would be a disgrace for an Englishman to chase the unarmed ship and let the *Providence* get away. But would this plan work?

All hands were busy aboard the *Providence*. The crew turned the little ship into the wind and then away from it, causing the boat to zigzag around the mighty English warship. Her small guns were loaded, but the captain knew better than to fire them straight into the thick hull of the English ship. There was no hope of firing through those oak planks.

Slowly, the heavy enemy ship turned about. A whole line of her guns roared. Her cannons boomed. But the heavy cannon balls splashed into the sea and not one hit the zigzagging little *Providence*.

89

Still Captain Paul waited. Each sailor held his breath. The English gunners were reloading. And then came the moment that Captain Paul had hoped for.

The *Providence* had stalled the English ship long enough so that the ammunition ship was out of danger. Captain Paul's plan had worked. At once Captain Paul shouted his next order, "Prepare to come about!"

The *Providence* started to move away from the enemy ship.

Suddenly a terrifying roar echoed from the enemy cannons.

The crew of the *Providence* waited anxiously. Would they be hit?

But each cannon ball fell into the water short of its mark.

"Return their fire," Captain Paul shouted.

And as the *Providence* fired at the English ship, Captain Paul gave his next order. "Full sail ahead."

The *Providence* raced forward, pulling away from the heavy English ship. The enemy could not catch them now.

The men of the *Providence* gave a mighty cheer. Captain Paul had outwitted his enemy. He had found a way to trick the English and save the ammunition ship.

Battle between John Paul Jones' *Bonhomme Richard* and the *Serapis.*
Painted especially for CHILDCRAFT by James M. Sessions.

The full name of Captain Paul was John Paul Jones, often called "The Father of the American Navy."

This exciting sea battle took place during the American Revolutionary War. It was courage and daring such as John Paul Jones displayed in this battle that made him a great naval officer. During another battle, Jones, with his ship on fire, was asked to surrender. His answer was, "I have not yet begun to fight!" These brave words have become a famous battle cry in the United States Navy.

John Paul Jones was born in Scotland. He went to sea at the age of twelve. He came to America in 1773 and was commissioned in the Navy two years later.

Jones was buried with honors at the United States Naval Academy, Annapolis, Maryland. He was elected to the United States Hall of Fame in 1925.

Some Other Books To Read

John Paul Jones, Fighting Sailor by Armstrong Sperry. Published by Random House, New York, 1953.

Story of John Paul Jones by Iris Vinton. Published by Grosset and Dunlap, Inc., New York, 1953.

TRAPPED IN A HAYLOFT

By Katharine J. Carter

As the coach rumbled over the bumpy road, Gilbert and his friend stretched out their legs and leaned back in the uncomfortable seat. Suddenly, they both sat up straight. A horseman had come out from a side road and was following their coach!

"Hurry!" Gilbert called to the driver of the coach.

Gilbert knew that his enemies were trying to stop him from sailing to America. The Americans were fighting for their freedom. Freedom was something in which Gilbert believed deeply. He was going to America to help in any way he could.

On and on they went with the horseman following, but coming no closer. The coach squeaked and groaned.

Gilbert had disguised himself in shabby clothes. He was taking this back road in the hope that the soldiers who were searching for him would not find him. Not far ahead, his ship was waiting. But this horseman might be one of the soldiers looking for him. Would he fail now?

"If we are stopped, what can I do?" Gilbert asked his friend.

"I don't know. Let's hope the horseman won't recognize you."

But Gilbert was desperate. His ship was waiting for him. He could not be stopped now!

As if reading Gilbert's thoughts, his friend said, "Don't worry. If that man was looking for you, he would surely have stopped us by now."

"I've been thinking of that, too," Gilbert said. "But there is too much at stake for me. I can't be sure."

After another mile, the horseman turned into a wooded path.

"At last!" Gilbert said. "A few more hours and we shall be on board my ship!"

His friend added, "With luck we will."

Gilbert nodded in agreement. He knew that they would not be safe until they reached the ship. They continued for several more miles, bumping and creaking along the roads.

At sunset, the driver of the coach called back to his two passengers, "A mile yonder we will come to an inn. I'll stop there and rest the horses for the night."

"No!" Gilbert shouted. "We cannot spare the time! We might be recognized!"

"Sorry, sir, but the horses can't go on forever," the driver insisted.

"I'll hire fresh horses."

"The inn doesn't have any for hire," the driver said with a shrug.

"We need food and rest, too," his friend reminded Gilbert.

"All right," Gilbert sighed.

If only they didn't have to stop. The soldiers who were looking for him would certainly search the inn. And that would be the end of his dream of fighting with General George Washington in America.

Before stepping down from the coach, Gilbert looked around. There was no one in sight.

"Go inside, eat, and sleep," he told his friend. "I will hide out here in the barn."

Inside the barn he found a ladder to the hayloft. He was about to climb the ladder when a young girl walked into the barn.

Gilbert stood still! What could he do? He had to tell her something.

He doffed his cap and bowed. "Permit me to sleep in the loft," he said softly. "It is very important that no one sees me."

The girl stared at him questioningly.

"I promise I mean no harm," Gilbert added quickly.

The girl smiled faintly. "As you want it," she said and went about her work.

Gilbert started up the ladder, then stopped. "If anyone asks about me, please do not tell them you have seen me," he said.

The young girl hurried out the door without answering.

Gilbert lay down in a heap of hay, but the fear of being discovered kept him from sleeping. The girl had already seen him. How many others had she told? Every time he heard voices or footsteps outside he sat up. He crawled around in the darkness trying to find a way to make a quick escape if he had to. Whenever he moved, the floor of the hayloft creaked loudly. When he found no way out but the ladder, he lay down again. He was anxious to be on his way. Every moment he spent in the hayloft made his chances of reaching the ship slimmer and slimmer. Many hours crept by before he finally dozed off.

At daybreak, he was awakened by the sound of horses' hooves. They halted near the barn! Men were speaking in hurried, commanding tones!

Gilbert peered through a small opening between the wallboards. Soldiers!

His heart pounded as he strained his ears. "He must have come this way," he heard one of the soldiers say.

Another one replied, "Maybe he went back to Paris."

Beads of perspiration formed on Gilbert's forehead. They were looking for him, and he could not escape without being seen.

The door of the inn opened. The young girl came out and walked toward the well.

His heart pounded faster. Surely she would give him away.

One of the soldiers called to her, "Have you seen a coach carrying a young man in a uniform?"

Gilbert held his breath. Perspiration trickled down his face.

"A coach went up the road about an hour ago," the girl answered in a clear voice.

The men thanked her and rode away quickly.

Overjoyed, Gilbert rushed outside. He thanked the girl and clasped her hands gratefully.

His friend joined him in the yard. They decided not to take the chance of traveling by coach again. They saddled the two coach horses and galloped off toward their waiting ship. At last Gilbert was on his way!

Gilbert, the young man in this story, was the Marquis de Lafayette. He was probably called Gilbert because his full name was too long. It was Marie Joseph Paul Yves Roch Gilbert du Motier.

This incident took place in 1777, shortly after the outbreak of the American Revolutionary War. Gilbert arrived in America and joined General Washington's staff as a major general. He led his troops to several victories for the Revolutionary Army. He returned to France a hero.

Lafayette became a prominent leader in the French Revolution which started in 1789. He continued to fight for freedom until his death in 1834.

He was buried in Paris, but some Americans who appreciated what he had done for their country covered his grave with earth from Bunker Hill, the scene of an important battle in the American Revolutionary War.

Marquis de Lafayette

Some Other Books To Read

Lafayette, Friend of America by Alberta Powell Graham. Published by Abingdon Press, Nashville, 1952.

The Story of Lafayette by Hazel Wilson. Published by Grosset and Dunlap, Inc., New York, 1952.

A NICKNAME THAT STUCK

By Virginia Barrett Novinger

In the early morning hours of June 28, 1778, a quiet had settled over the army camp. Scouts had come in earlier than usual from their rounds and were with General Greene at this very moment.

"What are they talking about?" the soldiers asked each other.

"They're probably planning a big battle."

"If there's much more fighting, we'll all be plumb tuckered out—or dead!"

"What's keeping the scouts in there so long?"

These and other questions remained unanswered until General Greene, himself, came out of his tent.

He told the men that General George Washington had ordered them to attack the British who were camped at Monmouth, New Jersey.

"If you listen, you can hear the rumble of their wagon trains scarcely a stone's throw from here," General Greene said.

Every man was silent. At first, they could hear only the birds chirping in the trees. But then, sure enough, the rumble of wooden wheels disturbing the quiet of the forest proved to the men that the British were, indeed, dangerously near.

It was hot. No breeze stirred. The white undersides of the maple leaves curled over the green topsides in wispy, feathery edgings.

The troops marched to the very edge of the British camp, guns and cannons ready. Soon the battle was raging.

General Greene allowed the men to take off their heavy, woolen uniform coats and fight in their shirt sleeves. Even this really did not lessen their suffering from the heat.

All that day Mary Ludwig Hays, known as Molly to her friends, did what she could for the wounded.

With an old pitcher in hand, she made hundreds of trips to and from the spring carrying water to the men. They would take a quick drink and go back to their guns.

The cries of the men could be heard over the roar of the battle, "Molly, here. Molly, pitcher, pitcher."

And brave Molly carried water and soothed the soldiers as best she could.

Molly's husband, John, was firing a cannon at the front lines.

Just as Molly was hurrying with a drink of water for her husband, she saw him fall at the foot of his cannon. She rushed quickly to his side. She felt his heart and found it was still beating. Molly realized then that he had not been shot, but had fallen from heat exhaustion as so many of the other men had done that day.

A soldier came up on his huge black horse. "Get this cannon out of the way," he shouted. "There is no one to fire it."

"I'll fire it," Molly cried. "I know how to load it."

The soldier looked at her and rode away.

Molly rammed ammmunition into the cannon and continued to pull the pin and fire the weapon all day. Her husband lay at her feet. She poured her last pitcher of water over his hot, burning face. Although she could hear the men crying, "Molly, pitcher, Molly, pitcher," she continued to stay at the cannon, firing round after round of shot.

At last the terrible fighting came to an end. The Americans were victorious!

Not until Molly was quite sure the battle was over did she leave her post at the gun. Then she pulled her husband away from the cannon's base, stretched him under a tree, and went to fetch some cool water for him. Finally, stretcher-bearers came and took John to the hospital.

Then Molly brought water to the other men. Pitcher by pitcher, she carried the precious water so desperately needed by the soldiers.

Near midnight she finally fell asleep.

The next day, the smoke of battle cleared, and the June sun shone again. Molly was surprised to hear General Greene calling her name as he rode through the camp.

"Molly," he said, as he reined in his horse. "General Washington wants to see you." He smiled encouragingly at the brave little woman.

A painting of the Battle of Monmouth by John Ward Dunsmore

"But look at me!" she said. "I can't let the general see me looking like this." Her hands flew to her hair, and she looked at her black dress, now dirty and torn. The blood of many soldiers was ground into the ragged skirt. The white collar that had long ago disappeared was being used as a bandage for some soldier's wound.

"I just couldn't face General Washington looking this way." Molly turned to go back to her husband.

"Molly," General Greene said, a bit sternly. "General George Washington is not going to see the dirt and grime. He is going to see a brave and wonderful woman. Now, come, you will have time to pretty up later on."

So, Molly went forward to see General George Washington. She was tired, but she stood straight and tall as the general announced that she would be given the rank of sergeant in the United States Army.

"Never have I seen a woman so brave," General Washington said.

A mighty roar from the throats of the thousands of men followed General Washington as he led cheer after cheer for the woman who had helped so courageously.

A tear slid down Molly's cheek.

She thanked the general, curtsied, and then went back to her husband's side.

From that time until the end of the Revolutionary War, Mary Ludwig Hays cared for the wounded men. She brought them water. She bandaged their wounds. She told them stories to make them laugh.

"Come now, soldier, drink from Molly's pitcher! You'll feel better for it," she would say.

"Molly, pitcher, Molly, pitcher," echoed through the hills and valleys in those days. It is sure that when Molly heard her name, she would be there to give comfort to the brave, fighting men.

Mary Ludwig Hays is remembered by the name the soldiers gave her during the hot June days in 1778. We now know her as "Molly Pitcher."

Some Other Books To Read

Of Courage and Valor by Jay Strong. Published by Hart Publishing Co., New York, 1955.

Great American Heroines by Arnold Dolin. Published by Hart Publishing Co., New York, 1960.

Molly Pitcher, Girl Patriot by Augusta Stevenson. Published by The Bobbs-Merrill Company, Inc., Indianapolis, 1960.

105

A DARING ATTACK

By Hazel Wilson

"All right, men," said the American general. "Here is our plan of attack."

The soldiers stood silently, listening to their general's orders.

"Just ahead of us is Stony Point," the general said.

The men could see the large cliff that loomed up in the darkness. At the top of the cliff was the British fort Stony Point.

"We are to attack Stony Point," the general went on. "The cliff is surrounded by water, but when the tide is low, which should be about midnight, we can wade across. We must have absolute silence, or our plan will fail.

"Our only chance is to surprise the British. We will advance in three columns. One column will climb the center of the cliff,

the other two columns will climb on the right and left sides. When the center column gets near the top of the cliff, they will begin firing. My plan is to make the British think that the center column is our main army. In the meantime, the left and right columns will continue up the cliff and attack the fort from both sides. I know you will all fight like men determined to be free."

When the general finished talking, the troops were divided into three columns.

It was close to midnight.

The general gave the signal. The columns moved toward the cliff. The water around the cliff was still fairly deep and the men

had to wade through water up to their waists. They held their muskets high above their heads and moved as quietly as possible. When they reached the cliff, they began the slow, steep climb toward the fort.

The general was with the left column. The tangle of branches up the side of the cliff was so thick that men had to chop through with axes. The sound of chopping was a great danger. If the British heard it, they would be able to stop the attack. Up, up they went. It was almost like scaling a wall, the cliff was so steep. But there was no sound from the fort.

Sleep sound and deep, British soldiers, thought the general. A wave of excitement swept over him, as often happened when he was in great danger. He remembered that one of his friends had said it would be impossible to capture Stony Point. We can and we shall, thought the general, as his column continued slowly up the cliff. And still the British were not aware of the coming attack.

In the quiet of the night the sound of chopping seemed loud. This time it reached the British. Gunfire came from the fort!

We have been discovered too soon, the general thought.

But then he saw that only the center column returned the fire. He hoped that the British did not yet know that columns were advancing from left and right.

We still have a chance, he thought.

By now the Americans had nearly reached the fort. There was bound to be hard fighting, but the attack seemed to be going according to plan. From the sound of the guns, it seemed that the British *had* been tricked into thinking that the center column was the whole attacking army.

The general was pushing his way through the last tangle of branches, when a shot split the air. He felt something like a hard slap on the side of his head. Then there was nothing but blackness.

He came to, lying just outside the branches, with two of his men bending over him.

"He's wounded badly, but he's not dead," he heard a voice say. Then his mind cleared, and he knew where he was and why he was there.

"We'll take him back down the hill," said another voice.

"No!" the general snapped.

Making a great effort, he sat up. "You will not take me back. Take me forward. If I die today, it will be at the head of my men."

Two men had to help him up the cliff. The troops were advancing rapidly now. The British were firing at all three columns of men.

But the British had discovered the plan too late. The left and right columns had nearly reached the fort by the time they were spotted.

The general was with the wave of men who swept into the fort from both sides.

The British fought bravely, but soon the battle was over. The general's plan had worked.

"The fort is ours," shouted the general above the cheers of his men.

Then weakness from his head wound overtook him. The general slumped to the ground again.

110

The general in this story was General Anthony Wayne, who was nicknamed "Mad Anthony" Wayne because he was never afraid to take risks. His attack in 1779 on Stony Point, an important British fort on the Hudson River, was considered to be one of the most daring of the Revolutionary War.

General Wayne recovered from his head wound and went on to fight bravely through the rest of the war. He once said, "I have always fought for a country I love and would defend with my last breath." The United States is a free country today partly because General Anthony Wayne inspired men to fight for their freedom.

Some Other Books To Read

Story of Anthony Wayne by Hazel Wilson. Published by Grosset and Dunlap, Inc., New York, 1953.

Anthony Wayne, Daring Boy by Augusta Stevenson. Published by The Bobbs-Merrill Company, Inc., 1953.

General Anthony Wayne

The SECRET

"Hide these papers carefully. Put them in your boot. If you are stopped by the Americans before you reach British headquarters, these papers will give away our plan," the general had said. "No, wait! I have a better idea!"

John André, a young British army major, could still remember the American general's idea. He hid the papers where the general had told him to.

The general had been gone for several hours already. André was at the home of an American, named Smith, who believed his country should remain under British rule. He was helping Major André return to British headquarters in New York with papers so secret and so valuable that they could mean defeat for the American forces.

"We will be passing through dangerous territory," Smith said. "You must wear civilian clothes."

"No!" André cried. "If I am caught in civilian clothes I'll be charged with spying. The penalty for that is death. But if I am captured in my uniform, I'll just be made a prisoner of war."

"If you wear your British uniform, you will have no chance of reaching New York," Smith pointed out. "You will be captured by the first Americans who see you."

André knew Smith was right. At last he agreed to wear civilian clothes.

Just before dark, André and Smith rode to Kings Point on horseback. They crossed the river on the ferry and headed toward New York. After a while, they stopped at a farmhouse for the night.

of the SPY'S BOOTS

By Charles P. Graves

André hardly slept. He was anxious to get to British headquarters with his valuable papers.

Early the next morning the two men continued their journey. Finally, Smith said he would go no farther. So André rode on alone, carrying the fate of America with him.

As he rode, he thought of the important papers he carried and of what could happen if he were caught.

He must make it to British headquarters. The outcome of the war might depend upon whether or not he was successful.

He was still several miles from New York when three young farmers stepped in front of his horse, barring the way. They were armed with muskets. André had no weapon.

"Get off your horse!" one of the men ordered.

André did not move.

"Get off that horse!" the man said again. He pointed his musket at André.

André dismounted and the men began to search him. He tried to appear calm, but his heart was pounding against his chest.

"Those papers," he thought. "Those terrible papers."

The young farmers went through his clothes and found nothing. André was beginning to believe he was safe.

"Take off your boots!" snapped one of the men.

André took off one boot. The men looked in it. It was empty. André prayed that now they would let him go.

But just then one of the men heard a slight rustle of paper. He noticed a bulge in André's stocking.

"Take off your stocking!"

André's hopes fell. When he removed his stocking, one of the men grabbed the papers and took a quick look.

"This man is a spy!" he cried.

The farmers found papers in both stockings. They made André a prisoner. By capturing him they had prevented the surrender of West Point and saved America from almost certain defeat in the Revolutionary War.

Major John André
This was sketched by André himself on the day before his execution.

The capture of Major John André was an important event in the history of the United States. For if André had arrived safely in New York, the United States as we know it today, would possibly not exist.

André was a spy. He had served the British well. But he was caught, and the penalty for spying is death. André was hanged on October 2, 1780. The important papers John André carried had been given to him by an American general, Benedict Arnold. General Arnold had agreed to betray his country by surrendering the American fort at West Point. The papers André carried would have told the British when to attack the fort. When he learned of André's capture, Benedict Arnold escaped to British headquarters in New York, and later went to England where he spent the rest of his life. Although Benedict Arnold had escaped, his treacherous plan had failed, and he was branded, forever, a traitor to his country.

Some Other Books To Read

First Book of the American Revolution by Richard Morris. Published by Franklin Watts, Inc., New York, 1956.

American Revolution by Bruce Lancaster. Published by Doubleday and Company, Inc., New York, 1957.

Spies of the Revolution by Katherine and John Bakeless. Published by J. B. Lippincott Co., Philadelphia, 1962.

The Swamp Fox's Secret Mission

By Dorfay

The general better known as "the Swamp Fox" read the last line of the message once more: "The mission must be secret to all except the generals."

He held the message to the open fire and watched it burn. Then he called for the drummer.

"Boy, how are your hands?" he asked.

A broad smile spread over the drummer's face. "Shall I roll the sticks? Do we march?"

The Swamp Fox stepped over to the youth and gave him a friendly slap on the shoulder. "We march."

"Booom-di-de-dum . . ." The drum sounded as if it were alive. At first, the boy beat the drum gently. As he became excited, he rolled the sticks faster and faster.

The small band of men gathered around with an eagerness that cheered the general.

"We have rested long enough, men," he said. "We have new orders. It's time to hit out against the Redcoats again." But the general did not mention what the orders were or to where they would be marching.

All day they moved south, through rice fields, through sand-beds, back into open fields, and finally into a thick pine forest. There they met Colonel Light-Horse Harry Lee with his legion of men. They had been ordered to join the general. The general gave the order to set up camp.

"Pitch the tents and we'll have a good night's sleep before we meet the Redcoats." The general walked through camp. He spoke warmly to the men.

"Well, now, you'd better put a patch in that boot, boy," he said to one soldier.

"Your horse needs a good combing, son," he advised another.

Then he gave words of encouragement to the men cleaning their muskets. "That's the way, lads. Keep your firing pieces sharp—you're about to get a chance to show your ability."

The Swamp Fox's men knew that they must be going into the thick of battle in the morning. The general always spent the night before a battle with them. They wondered where they would be going—what battle they would fight.

The men were awake before dawn. They broke camp and waited for orders.

"On to Nelson's Ferry," the general's voice rang out.

By nightfall they had passed Nelson's Ferry and reached Fort Watson, a major British stronghold.

Now the men knew the secret. They were to capture Fort Watson and cut off the British communications. There would be some real fighting now.

"Pitch the tents among the hawthorn trees, out of range of the fort," the general ordered.

"Lee, have your men fire at the fort. That will give me an idea of how strong they are."

A volley of shot from Lee's riflemen brought musket and cannon fire in return. The general knew this would not be a quick battle. The fort was a well-constructed log stockade with cannons and much ammunition. Without cannons the Americans could not outfire the British. The Swamp Fox would have to outwit them.

"Sarg," he called to one of his trusted marksmen. "Take some men over by that lake. It is out of range of the fort so you won't need much cover. And don't let a single Redcoat take a drop of water!"

The Swamp Fox smiled and chuckled to himself as he turned to Light-Horse Harry. "This may not be as bad as we thought. We can just sit here and take it easy till they get thirsty!"

There was merriment in the general's camp that night and during the day that followed. Now it seemed to be just a waiting game. Occasionally there would be the whine of a rifle shot as someone attempted to run from the fort to the lake. The only other sounds were those made by the men tending to the ordinary tasks of camp life.

Then another sound came from inside the fort. There was a hush in the American camp as they listened.

"What can they be doing?" Lee asked the general.

"I don't know—" the general started to say. Then he recognized the sound. It was the sound of digging. "They outfoxed me!" he groaned. "They are digging a well!"

"Now what do we do?"

"I don't know," replied the general. "Their cannons are too powerful for us. We can't move any closer to the fort."

Every muscle in his face was tight as he thrust his hands deep into his pockets and paced around the tents. The men dared not speak to him. They had seen their leader deep in thought before.

The Swamp Fox knew there must be a way to defeat the British commander. Maybe one of the men would have an idea. He stopped and asked one and then another what he thought they could do. The general considered each suggestion, but went on pacing and thinking.

Then Major Hezekiah Maham had an idea. The general listened with interest to the major's plan. A twinkle came into his eyes. He straightened his back, smiled, and took a deep breath before he gave the order, "Lee, have a squadron go to the plantations in the area and get all the axes they can lay their hands on! If the Redcoats can build, so can we!"

Excitement spread through the camp when the men saw the change in the Swamp Fox.

"The 'Fox' is at it again!" they whispered.

They had no idea what they would build, but whatever it was, they were ready to build it.

When the men returned with the axes, the general called Major Maham. "Major," he said, "this is your idea. Take as many men as you need. Build me a tower to beat all towers."

A tower! The word spread quickly among the men.

Work started immediately. Major Maham sent men to chop down trees. He sent others to gather ropes and leather straps. Holes were dug to give a good foundation to the tower. The men laughed when they saw the British looking over the walls of the fort at them.

"Just wait," they yelled. "We'll show you!" Though truly they were not sure what they would show them.

For hours the sound of splitting logs filled the woods. The men worked quickly, eager to find out what the secret plan would be.

Finally, the tower reached the desired height. The men reinforced the front of the tower with a solid wall of timber. While they were tying in the last logs, the general was already at work preparing for the maneuver that would follow.

He called to his best riflemen, "All right, men. When you climb onto that tower, you will be able to see every nook and cranny in the whole fort!"

A whoop and yell went through the American camp. Now they would be able to fight as if there were no fort at all. They

would have more protection than those in the fort. Their rifles had longer range than the British muskets, and the buckshot from the muskets could not pierce the shield of logs.

The general's men climbed the tower and the firing began.

Shots rained into the fort.

The British troops crouched in the shadows of the high wall facing the tower. That was the only safe spot.

But there was no way for them to escape or shoot back.

When the general saw that they were safe, he sent several of his men with axes to the wall of the fort. With the bullets of their own men whining above their heads, they chopped away at the wall. The British could do nothing. They continued to hide behind the wall.

Soon the Americans had chopped their way through. The British stood helpless before them. The battle was over!

Shouts of joy went through the American camp as they saw a white flag hoisted over Fort Watson. The British had surrendered. The mission was completed.

"Roll that drum, boy," the soldiers called out. "The Swamp Fox has done it again!"

The general called "the Swamp Fox" was General Francis Marion. He was named "the Swamp Fox" because of his daring raids. He and his men would dart out of the marshes to strike a severe blow against the British, and then vanish into the swamps again. The Swamp Fox was loved and admired by his men because of his daring and bravery and because of the fair way he treated them.

The surrender of Fort Watson, a vital British fort in South Carolina, was an important victory for the Americans during the Revolutionary War. It cut off communications between the two main British headquarters in Camden and Charleston, South Carolina, and helped turn the tide of battle in the southern colonies toward the American forces.

South Carolina Swampland

Some Other Books To Read

Francis Marion: Young Swamp Fox by William O. Steele. Published by The Bobbs-Merrill Company, Inc., Indianapolis, 1954.

Francis Marion: Swamp Fox of the Revolution by Beryl Williams and Samuel Epstein. Published by Julian Messner, Inc., New York, 1956.

Swamp Fox of the Revolution by Stewart Holbrook. Published by Random House, Inc., New York, 1962.

Dash Into Danger

By A. D. Lewis

"Beat you home, Betty!" boasted a young boy, tugging at the arm of a tall girl. Without a word, the two of them rushed through the gates.

Across the clearing—for almost a hundred yards—the figures sped, and the figure that was in front all the way was marked by a flash of white petticoats. As she ran, Betty clutched her long skirt with both hands, pulled it tight, and held it above her swift-moving legs. She ran, never slacking her speed until she reached the yard in front of a cabin. Then she dropped, laughing and panting, onto the grass. The boy pounded up and dropped beside her, gasping for breath.

"Some day I'm going to beat you," vowed the boy. "When I get bigger—"

"When you are as old as I am, Johnny, your legs will be six inches longer than mine. Then I won't dare to race you," Betty said comfortingly.

Five years ago, Betty had come to Fort Henry to live with her brother Ebenezer and his family. She had grown from a bright little girl into a lovely young woman. Although the women of the settlement thought Betty, at eighteen, was far too old to be running races with the boys, they couldn't dislike her. She had a quick smile and was willing to take on any task.

For the past five years Fort Henry had never been completely free from the danger of attack. Betty's brother, Ebenezer, had been the first white man to settle here on the Ohio River and was the recognized leader of the soldiers and settlers who followed him. He had treated the Indians with respect and he had received respect in return.

But since the Indians had been stirred up by the British, the settlers had not dared to relax completely. Men carried rifles along with their axes when they cleared the land. Women kept a sharp eye on their children every minute. And whenever the big bell outside Ebenezer's cabin began to ring, every man snatched his rifle and the women rounded up the children and they all ran—day or night—to the protection of the fort.

Darkness came swiftly in September. The candles were lighted by the time Ebenezer and his brother Silas came home. The family gathered around the big table for supper. The night was still. The door stood open. Suddenly, a figure appeared in the doorway.

One of Ebenezer's Indian scouts stepped into the room. His clothes were dripping wet. He barely nodded to the others in the room as he clutched Ebenezer's shoulder. "Redcoats—and at least two hundred Indians!" he whispered hoarsely. "They are on the way to the fort. I had to swim the river to get here ahead of them. You haven't got much time!"

Ebenezer rushed out of the cabin and rang the warning bell. Almost immediately flickers of light could be seen through cabin windows and doorways. The settlers gathered their children, rifles, and whatever food they could carry and hurried to the stockade.

Ebenezer stayed in the cabin with the Indian scout, and three others. The cabin was halfway between the fort and the edge of the forest. They would guard the powder supply that was hidden beneath the floorboards and hold off the attack for as long as possible. Silas led the rest of the settlers to the fort.

The attack began at dawn. The British fired volley after volley from the edge of the forest. All day the wild yells of the Indians filled the air. They tried again and again to storm the fort only to be cut down by the crossfire from the fort and the cabin.

Betty worked hard inside the fort. Most of the day she crouched against the wall of the fort, loading rifles for the men. When it was time to give out water, Betty ladled it out by the dipperful and handed it to each man. When she was told to rest, she helped the women tear cloth into strips for bandages.

At nightfall the enemy withdrew. From the walls the settlers could see the Indian council fires down by the river's edge. The men began to relax a little. Women prepared food over open fires and tended the soldiers who had been wounded. Children came out of the blockhouse for their first breath of fresh air. At last, in the cooling darkness, quiet returned.

Betty thought of the important role her

family had played that day. In the cabin, Ebenezer and his companions had held off the attack. Betty's brother, Silas, had been in charge of defending the fort. And even young Johnny had helped Betty keep the men supplied with gunpowder and water.

The attack was even fiercer the next day. The British kept up a constant stream of fire. The Indians became more frenzied than ever. They were angry because they could not reach the walls. They used arrows and spears and stones. Flaming arrows fell everywhere in the fort. But as quickly as they fell, they were snatched and thrown to the ground and stamped on until they smoldered harmlessly.

Late in the afternoon the enemy drew back. The British lay in little groups under the trees. The Indians crouched near the edge of the clearing, resting while their leaders held council again.

Betty's brother Silas jumped down from the wall, waving for the men to follow. "Johnny," he shouted. "You keep watch while we have our own council of war."

Johnny climbed to the top of the wall. The settlers gathered around Silas whose face was grim. "I don't know what they are planning, but I do know we cannot withstand even one more big rush. We have only enough gunpowder for a few more rounds."

Betty spoke up, "There is powder in the cabin—"

"I know," Silas replied.

The men looked around at each other. Before anyone could speak, Betty was in the middle of them. "There are so few of you men," she cried. "And so many women and children to defend here! Let me go!"

The men refused her. Not one of them could think of a girl doing such a dangerous thing.

But Betty went on quickly, "A woman can be spared—a man cannot. I know I can do it—I've run that distance a hundred times!"

In the silence that followed, Johnny's voice came down to them. "She can run faster than anybody in this fort," he cried, never taking his eyes away from the enemy.

Without waiting for an answer, Betty moved swiftly toward the gate. Two soldiers followed her. They pulled the thick wooden beams from the gate and swung it open just enough for her to slip through. Men and women alike rushed to the wall to watch Betty's dangerous run.

Swiftly as a deer Betty ran across the clearing. She felt as though her feet had wings. She was almost halfway to Ebenezer's cabin before the Indians spotted her. Then a shout went up.

"Squaw!" hooted the Indians. It struck them as hilarious that a woman should be running toward the cabin.

Ebenezer had the door open. He reached out and pulled her inside. "What is wrong? What has happened at the fort?"

"We need gunpowder," Betty gasped. "We haven't enough!"

Ebenezer led the girl to a chair. He brought a dipper of water for her to drink. Then he poured some water over a piece of cloth and held the cloth to her forehead.

"We have plenty," he said quietly. "But how much can you carry?"

Betty looked up at her brother in dismay. It had never occurred to her that enough powder to save the fort would be more than one girl could carry.

"I'll go," Ebenezer said instantly. "You can't carry enough powder for the fort."

"No!" said Betty. "We need you men right here. I must go back. If the Indians see a man, they will shoot. Just one shot can set off the powder and lose the whole fort!"

She looked at Ebenezer. "The Indians didn't shoot at me once," she said earnestly. "They thought it was funny to see a girl running. Maybe I can get back before they realize what I have—if I can only find some way to carry it."

Without a word Ebenezer crossed the room and took a tablecloth from the drawer of a chest. "Stand up," he ordered. He took two corners and tied them securely around his sister's waist like an apron. "Hold this and tell me when it gets too heavy."

As Betty held the other two corners, Ebenezer poured gunpowder into this made-up apron. Then he tied the corners together over her wrists. Ebenezer opened the door cautiously.

"Good luck, little sister!" he whispered, as he brushed a kiss across her cheek.

They closed the door and Betty started toward the fort. Her burden weighed her down. This time her feet did not feel as though they had wings. Before she had gone ten yards, the Indians began shouting again. But this time they did not laugh or think she was funny. Now they saw that a trick had been played on them.

A rain of arrows and bullets and stones and spears began falling around her. Betty remembered an old trick Ebenezer had taught her. She began running a zigzag course. Every time she turned, the heavy load she carried bumped against her legs. Her wrists felt as though they would break. An arrow went by her head with a hiss. She ducked a little and tried to keep her body between the enemy and the gunpowder. She would rather get a bullet in a leg or an arm than have the powder explode. Once she stepped into a hole and a flash of pain rushed up from her ankle. By some miracle, though, she did not fall.

Then she heard another shout. It came from the fort that loomed up before her. At last she was inside!

Now there was enough powder. The settlers at Fort Henry withstood the siege. And there, on September 13, 1782, ended the last battle of the American Revolution.

The girl who made this daring run was Betty Zane, an American heroine. When Betty died, she was buried near the spot where Fort Henry stood. A statue of Betty carrying the gunpowder marks her grave. Betty Zane is an example of the bravery and the courage of the pioneer women who helped to build America.

The town of Zanesville, Ohio, was named for Ebenezer Zane and his family, who settled there in 1797.

Some Other Books To Read

They Made America Great by Edna McGuire. Published by The Macmillan Co., New York, 1957.

Short Stories of Famous Women by Pearl A. Wanamaker. Published by Noble and Noble, Publishers, Inc., New York, 1949.

Engraving of Fort Henry, where the last battle of the
Revolutionary War was fought. Fort Henry stood in
what is now Wheeling, West Virginia.

A Walk Through Danger

By Mary J. Leake

Jemima Johnson woke with a start when she heard a commotion outside her cabin. She rushed out to see what was wrong. Settlers were coming from all directions in the fort to gather in front of Captain Craig's cabin.

Captain Elijah Craig, leader of the fort at Bryan's Station in Kentucky, was talking excitedly. "Indians have been spotted," Captain Craig said. "There may be hundreds of them outside the fort. We may be completely surrounded."

In a few minutes all the settlers—men, women, boys, and girls—were gathered around Captain Craig. Everyone thought of the same thing—WATER. Yesterday's supply was gone. There was only one spring nearby. And it lay at the foot of a hill outside the fort.

Already the first streaks of morning light were creeping across the sky. Captain Craig spoke tensely, "We must have water. We can't defend the fort without it." His face was drawn with worry as he added, "The Indians will probably attack at sunrise. So there's not much time. They know that the women usually go for water. If we men go to the spring this morning, they'll know that we suspect them. Then they'll have no reason to wait until sunrise to surprise us. They'll attack at once. And we need all the time we can get to prepare for the attack."

Everyone was silent for a while.

Then Jemima Johnson spoke up, "I'll go for water!"

Her voice did not betray the fear she felt. As she started for the water buckets, she glanced at the other women.

I'll go with you," one woman called out.

In a moment all the women and girls in the fort were picking up their water buckets and dippers.

"We'll beat the Indians at their own game! We'll fool them," Jemima said defiantly. "We'll go to the spring as we always do. We'll pretend that we don't know they're out there hiding."

Jemima, and her daughters Sally and Betsy, led the way out of the stockade. The rest of the women followed them.

As the men swung the big gate of the fort open, Captain Craig whispered, "God be with you."

He saw a glimmer of hope in Jemima's words about deceiving the Indians. But he knew all too well that the trip to the spring might end in a massacre. Were the

Indians planning to wait until sunrise as he suspected? And could the women fool them?

The little band of women strolled along the zigzag path that led to the spring. They chatted and giggled as they usually did during this daily chore. Jemima pretended to tease and joke with Betsy and Sally who followed closely behind her.

Soon they went down the hill and were out of sight of the fort. There could be no help from the men now!

At last they reached the spring. The spring was not deep enough for them to dip their wooden buckets into the water. Each bucket had to be filled with a dipper. Although not a second was wasted, it seemed that the spring had never flowed so slowly. Jemima sensed that the Indians were very close.

At last every bucket was filled, and they started the long walk back to the fort.

The men, who had waited anxiously to swing the big gate open, sighed with relief as the women and girls filed into the fort. They knew the Indians had been fooled. But there was little time for rejoicing.

Each man took his post. Every boy who was big enough held a rifle. The women and girls set to work molding bullets. The guards watched the woods tensely.

Then it was sunrise.

Suddenly, the Indians darted from their hiding places, whooping and yelling. Waving their tomahawks, they rushed up the hillside toward the fort.

But the settlers were ready for them. One after another, volleys of rifle shots crashed from the portholes of the fort. The women stood by to reload guns and pass them to the men.

The surprised Indians, who had planned to catch the settlers off guard, ran in all directions to escape the gunfire. Soon the only Indians in sight were the dead ones on the grassy slope.

All during the night, the Indians kept the settlers awake with small attacks. When they saw that they could not take the fort by forcing an entry, they shot flaming arrows over the walls.

139

Instantly, the flames spread around the wooden fort. The settlers worked with all their strength, using the water the women had brought to put out the fires.

Finally, the fort was saved. At daybreak the Indians slipped out of the woods as quietly as they had come.

Without the water carried by the brave women and girls, the fort at Bryan's Station could not have been saved.

During the Revolutionary War years, the early Kentucky settlers had to defend themselves against many Indian attacks. This story was about one of those attacks.

About five miles northeast of Lexington, Kentucky, there is a memorial wall at the Bryan's Station spring. The inscription on the wall reads: "In Honor of the Women of Bryan's Station Who, on the 16th of August, 1782, Faced a Savage Host in Ambush, and, with a Heroic Courage . . . Obtained from THIS SPRING the water that Made Possible the Successful Defense of that Station."

The names of Jemima Suggett Johnson and Sally and Betsy Johnson head the list of names of women and girls who made the trip to the spring.

Some Other Books To Read

Frontier Living by Edwin Tunis. Published by The World Publishing Company, Cleveland and New York, 1961.

Westward Adventure by William O. Steele. Published by Harcourt, Brace and World, Inc., New York, 1962.

THE
BROKEN
PROMISE

By Mea Underwood

Alexander slammed the door shut and shouted, "Pierre, Pierre!"

Pierre, the boatman, came running around the side of the shed. Seeing Alexander's determined look, he stopped short.

"Pierre, we're going down the river to visit the Indian camps," Alexander announced. "I'm going to find out for myself what has happened to the fur pelts the Indians promised to bring us. We have nothing to show for our work but an empty shed."

Pierre nodded gravely. He knew that inside the shed, there were only a few piles of goods remaining from the great supply that they had carried with them into the wilderness. All the blankets, kettles, knives, mirrors, and tobacco had been given to the Indians. In return, the Indians had promised that when fall came to the Canadian wilderness, they would bring pelts of fur. But fall had come and gone, and there was no sign of the Indians or their furs.

Everyone in the little fort wondered why the Indians had broken their promise.

"Perhaps they have already traded their furs to someone else," said Pierre.

Alexander scowled, "If they have, we will fight them. They made a promise, and it's up to us to see that they keep it."

"But the river is nearly frozen," argued Pierre.

Alexander looked toward the river. Pierre was right. Frost bent the boughs of the willows along the shore. Thick ice covered the banks. And as the two men watched, blocks of ice crashed from the banks and were carried down the river by the swift current.

"It won't be easy," Alexander said. "But if we leave at once, we should be able to make the trip. Next week will be too late. By then the river will be covered with ice, and we will be stranded here all winter."

"Yes, you are right," Pierre answered. "We must go now."

"I want one of the small canoes," Alexander told Pierre. "We need to move as quickly as possible."

"I will get it ready," Pierre answered.

An hour later Alexander came down to the water's edge. He was bundled in his heavy coat.

Alexander stepped into the front of the canoe, Pierre into the back. They eased the canoe into the center of the river. The current began to carry them downstream. Mighty chunks of ice, broken away from the shore, swept around them. The river roared.

Alexander looked around at Pierre's grave face.

"Very bad!" Pierre shouted above the noise of the water.

"If we are careful, we can do it," Alexander called back.

He was pleased to see Pierre nod in agreement. But there was no time for talking. If the racing ice blocks struck their canoe, it would be smashed and their chances for swimming to safety would be slim indeed.

Alexander watched the rushing water like a hawk. His eyes darted back and forth, watching, watching.

The canoe raced along, swaying in the wake of the drifting ice. They were making good progress. They would soon be ap-

proaching the first Indian camp. It would not be long before they would know exactly what had become of their furs.

Alexander glanced toward the riverbank. A huge ice block had broken off the bank and was being swept midstream. At first it did not seem any different from the others. But when he looked a second time, he realized with horror that they were directly in its path. It was moving toward them with such speed that he could see no way to dodge it.

Alexander gave a shout of warning to Pierre.

But Pierre held his paddle above the water. He was paralyzed with fear.

"Pierre!" Alexander shouted again, his own paddle cutting the gray water with frantic strokes.

The shout brought Pierre back to his senses. In an instant he had thrust his paddle into the water. With all his great strength,

Pierre struggled to steer the canoe out of the path of the ice block.

The canoe swerved so suddenly that Alexander lost his balance and nearly toppled into the icy river. He kept paddling fiercely, expecting the tiny canoe to be smashed to bits at any moment.

But the collision didn't come! Was it possible that the ice block had missed the canoe?

Alexander did not dare look. Every muscle was strained to the limit with the effort of paddling.

But, finally, he glanced behind him. Out of the corner of his eye, he saw that the ice block had just barely missed the back of the canoe. The canoe began to bob crazily. They must keep it afloat!

Then, suddenly, they were safe, racing down the river, leaving the ice block behind.

"That was close!" shouted Pierre.

Alexander had no time to answer. Before them, the crude log huts of the Indian camp swept into view.

The two tired men paddled the canoe toward the camp. As soon as they reached the shore, Alexander leaped from the canoe and started to march toward the log huts.

Two Indians hurried toward him. As Alexander tramped along, he saw other Indians coming out of the huts. He could tell that they were excited.

In a moment Alexander was surrounded by Indians. He stood firm and unafraid.

The leader of the group was a tall, fierce-looking Indian. He motioned his people to stop chattering. A moment passed before the Indian spoke.

"Does the white man want the fur pelts my people have worked so hard to trap?" he finally asked.

Alexander was stunned. But quickly he replied, "Yes, of course! Why have you not brought them to me?"

There was another long silence, and then the Indian began to chuckle. Laughter started on the outskirts of the group and spread rapidly among the braves. Even the squaws began to snicker. Children rolled in merriment on the snow.

Alexander thought that they must all have gone crazy. What could possibly have been so funny?

Finally the Indian leader spoke up, "We thought you would come for the fur pelts. You thought we would bring them to you. So we both sat and wondered and wondered, and waited and waited, and no one did anything."

So that had been the trouble! The Indians had not broken their promise after all. Alexander tilted his head back and joined in the laughter.

"Come," the tall Indian said. "We wish to show you the pelts we have stored for you. They are many and beautiful."

Alexander Mackenzie, the young man in this story, was a well-known Canadian trader, explorer, and author. This incident happened nearly two hundred years ago in the wilderness of the Canadian Northwest.

In his trips through the wilderness, Alexander discovered many things about the Indians of Canada.

In 1793, he became the first man to cross the northern part of Canada and reach the Pacific Ocean.

After his many years of exploration, Alexander Mackenzie wrote books about his exciting adventures.

Some Other Books To Read

Knight of the Wilderness by Maxine Shore and M. M. Oblinger. Published by Dodd, Mead & Co., New York, 1943.

First Northwest Passage by Walter O'Meara. Published by Houghton Mifflin Co., Boston, 1960.

Sir Alexander Mackenzie

The King's Spear

By Mea Underwood

"Do you know that Kule and Piima are plotting against you?" Koa asked.

Kamehameha, the mighty King of the island of Hawaii, met his friend's steady gaze but said nothing. He was too shocked.

"I do not believe it," Kamehameha finally answered. "I see those chiefs every day. We talk and smile and are the best of friends."

"But it is true," Koa insisted. "They have been overheard whispering in the forest. They plan to kill you, and join your enemy the King of Maui. Then they will fight against us."

Before the day was over, two other friends had told the King the same thing.

That night, the King's servant whispered to him, "Tonight Kule and Piima are meeting in one of the lava caves at the foot of the mountain. Shall I send your guards after them? Or should I bring Kule and Piima to you so that you may question them?"

Kamehameha shook his head. "Do nothing," he told the servant. "I need to prove to myself that the two chiefs are planning to kill me."

After all the people in the village had gone to sleep, Kamehameha took his great spear and slipped out of his grass house. No one saw him go.

Kamehameha ran swiftly toward the meeting place of the two chiefs. He knew the country well. He hoped that the darkness would not slow him down so that he would be too late.

But the bright moon shone and guided his feet. The moonlight helped him find his way.

All the while he ran, Kamehameha carried the powerful spear in his hand. Under the laws of Hawaii, no one but the King could touch this spear. Anyone else who touched it would die. Kamehameha thought of this as he ran toward the caves. It reminded him that the honor of his position carried with it the responsibility to be fair and brave.

When the King reached the foot of the mountain, he hurried from one cave to another. He listened silently at the entrance of several caves. No sound greeted his ears except the wind's sighing.

All at once, he heard faraway voices. He stopped, grasping his spear. Then he moved ahead carefully toward the sound of the voices.

Kamehameha stooped down and found a cave opening hidden by small trees. The voices were coming from inside. They were the voices of Kule and Piima! The cave opening was so small, a person had to crawl to enter it.

A good place, indeed, to plan a murder, thought Kamehameha.

Several times, he heard his name, and then he heard the words, "When we kill Kamehameha. . . ."

The voices became softer, and the King could no longer make out the words. But now he knew that the reports were true! What should he do? Should he crawl into the cave with his mighty spear and kill Kule and Piima? Or would it be better to accuse them in front of the whole village so the people would know what the two were planning?

Suddenly, the King had an idea.

Taking his spear, he drove it deep into the soft earth at the cave's entrance. He placed it in such a way that no man could crawl in or out of the cave without touching the spear. And to touch the spear meant death! Then the King turned and started back toward the village.

In the moonlight the spear seemed to quiver as though it were alive.

Kule and Piima planned late into the night. At last they grew sleepy. Since they knew it would be many hours before dawn, they huddled together in the damp cave and slept.

Kule was the first to awaken. He could see a tiny ray of light filtering in from the mouth of the cave. He sat up in alarm. They must have overslept!

He roused Piima. There was no time to lose! They must get back to the village. They must look as though they had spent the night stretched out in their grass houses.

"Come!" Kule commanded, and led the way to the mouth of the cave.

As they crept along single file, the light grew brighter and brighter as they approached the mouth of the cave. They could even hear a bird singing.

Suddenly, Kule reared back on his knees. He struck his head on the top of the cave. Something had startled him terribly.

"What is it?" Piima asked. "Why do you stop?"

Kule rubbed his head with his hand. He did not answer.

Piima peered outside. He saw something stretched across the opening. It looked like a huge stick.

"What is it?" Piima asked again.

"I'm not sure," Kule replied. "But I have a terrible fear."

"Why do you have a terrible fear?" Piima asked. Why was a big stick that had fallen across the entrance so frightening? They could simply push it aside and crawl out.

Kule began to move forward again. Piima followed.

But once more Kule stopped.

"Go on! Go on!" Piima urged, eager to get out of the cave.

"We can't," Kule said in a choked voice.

"Push the stick over. It is simple."

"That stick is the King's sacred spear!"

"Auwe!" (Alas, indeed!) was all Piima exclaimed.

It was one thing to plot to kill the King, secretly, in a deep cave. It was quite another thing to face his deadly spear. Neither man spoke for a long moment.

At last Kule whispered, "What can we do?"

"Is the King out there?" Piima wondered.

"I will thrust my head around the spear," Kule said. "Then I can see out."

"But do not touch the spear! Never touch the spear!"

Kule poked his head under the great shaft.

The sky was clear. Birds sang. The grass waved in the breeze. No one was there!

"We are alone!" he whispered, pulling his head back in.

"If the spear is here, the King must have brought it," Piima said. "No one else would have dared to touch it. The King knows that something was going on in this cave last night."

A deep silence followed.

Then Kule whispered, "If we crawl out, we will have to touch the spear. According to the law, that means death."

"But if we stay here, we shall die."

"We could crawl out and run away to the mountains."

"We would be tracked down by the King's guards," Piima finished hopelessly.

All at once Kule spoke up, "We could slip into the village quietly. Even if the King knows we were in the cave last night, how can he know we were planning to kill him?"

Neither of them realized that their voices had carried through the quiet night, and that the King had overheard them.

"We have told no one our plans," Kule reminded Piima. "I have not told a soul. Have you?"

Piima shook his head, "Naturally I have not told!"

"Then I think we should push the spear aside and go back to the village as though nothing has happened."

"But the King will know we touched his spear!"

"If the King thinks we are friendly to him, he will believe us if we say the wind blew it over in the night," Kule replied.

155

Piima gazed at the spear.

Kule studied it, too. All their lives they had been brought up to believe that they must obey their laws. Could they now touch the spear?

"You are closest," Piima said to Kule. "Give the spear a push."

Kule sat there. He did not lift his hand.

"Well," Piima urged. "Go on!"

Kule turned and stared sharply at Piima. "I will not touch it alone," he said. "We must push it over together."

Piima answered the look with an equally fierce one. "If we are to get to the village in time, we must get out of here!" he warned.

Piima thrust his hand around Kule's shoulder. His fingers grazed the smooth wooden shaft. His hands felt as though they were on fire. He made sure that Kule's hand was on the spear, too.

"Now push!" he commanded.

With all their might they pressed against the spear. It wobbled for a moment, then fell with a thud.

"Come!" Kule ordered.

Both men scrambled out of the cave. They were afraid to look at the mighty spear, lying on the ground.

"Quickly!" Kule said. The chiefs hurried into the woods.

The villagers were assembling when Piima and Kule slipped into the crowd of men. Kamehameha saw them come. He now had the final proof that they were traitors. The sacred spear must right now be lying on the earth!

For awhile, the King pretended to take no note of them. Finally, he turned and fixed his stern look on Kule and Piima.

Pointing toward them, he asked, "Who are these men who have come into our village?"

Both chiefs gave a guilty start.

There was a dreadful pause. All eyes were fastened on the pair.

Almost in one voice the two traitors spoke up. "You know who we are. We are Kule and Piima, your loyal chiefs."

Kamehameha looked at them for a long moment. Then he shook his head. "Alas," he said. "That is impossible. The chiefs are dead."

Were they really dead? No one knows. It may have been that the traitors, Kule and Piima, were put to death for their treachery. Or it may have been that with Kamehameha's words, no one ever looked at or spoke to them again. And though they may have seemed to be alive because they walked, and heard, and breathed, no one ever again paid attention to them.

Kamehameha was a brave warrior and a wise ruler. Today, Hawaii is part of the United States. But at one time it was just a group of islands in the Pacific Ocean that Kamehameha united into a strong kingdom. When the white men came to the islands, Kamehameha helped his people learn the ways of the white men, and helped the white men learn the ways of Hawaii. Once he had built his strong kingdom and won peace, he worked very hard to preserve it.

Some Other Books To Read

Hawaii, the Aloha State by Helen Bauer. Published by Doubleday and Company, Inc., New York, 1960.

First Book of Kings by Douglas Newton. Published by Franklin Watts, Inc., New York, 1961.

"ARREST

By Mabel-Ruth Jackson

Three hard bangs on the front door suddenly broke the morning's quiet.

Mr. Rouzy was working in his study. Who could be visiting him so early in the morning and knocking so rudely? He listened as Caleb, his house servant, went to the door. He heard a loud voice demand, "Where is your master?"

"Wait here, gentlemen, and I'll tell him you're here," Caleb's voice sounded frightened.

"None of that, my man! Bring him here immediately!"

Mr. Rouzy hurried into the hall. He recognized the two men who stood there. One was President Washington's agent for that district of Virginia. He looked angry and threatening. The other man was sheriff of a nearby town.

"There he is, sheriff. Arrest that man," the agent shouted, pointing at Mr. Rouzy.

"Gentlemen, please," said Mr. Rouzy. "I'm sure there must be some mistake. I've done nothing wrong."

"Nothing wrong, ha! You're Mr. Reuben Rouzy, aren't you?" the agent asked with a sneer.

"I am, as you well know," Mr. Rouzy answered.

The agent shook his finger at Mr. Rouzy. "Yes, and I well know that I asked you some time ago to repay the money you owe President Washington. I also know that you refused!"

"I did not refuse," Mr. Rouzy said, noticing the angry look on the agent's face. "I told you that I could not pay it at that time. But I said that I was sure I would have the money in another year when I had sold my crops."

Mr. Rouzy saw that his wife and his children had slipped into the hall. They looked confused and frightened.

"The money must be paid now!" the agent shouted. "You could sell your large estate here and—"

Mr. Rouzy interrupted the agent. "You know I would not get half of what this estate is worth. If I sold now, my wife and children and I would have nowhere to live. We would be penniless."

"That's no concern of mine!" shouted the agent. "I don't want any excuses. I am here as the agent of President Washington to collect the money you owe him. Unless you pay me now, I will take you to the debtors' prison. Well?"

Mr. Rouzy's face was strained and white, but he spoke proudly, "I can say no more than I have said to you before. I will repay the money I owe General Washington. But I cannot do it now."

"Sheriff!" the agent ordered. "Give him the warrant! We are taking you to jail, Reuben Rouzy!"

The children broke into sobs. Ethan, the oldest of them, started toward his father. His mother, tears running down her cheeks, held him back.

The sheriff handed Mr. Rouzy the warrant. "I'm afraid I'll have to arrest you, sir. These papers are official orders."

Mr. Rouzy took the warrant and called to Ethan, "Son," he said, resting his hand on the boy's shoulder. "While I am away, I want you to take my place as much as you can. Help your mother with the other children and do anything else that needs to be done."

Ethan, holding back his tears, stood straight. "I will, Father," he promised.

Mr. Rouzy hugged his weeping wife tenderly and kissed the children. "Be good and obey your mother," he told them.

They all watched sadly from the front porch as the three men mounted their horses and rode away.

Mr. Rouzy was taken straight to jail and was placed in a cell by himself. He sat down on the hard jail bed and tried to understand everything that had happened.

How could his friend, General Washington, have treated him this way? George Washington had been President for only a short time. Mr. Rouzy still thought of him as the brave general

who, in spite of losses and hardships, had led the colonial army to victory.

And now, it seemed Washington had turned against him. How could it be possible?

Mr. Rouzy stood up and sadly looked at the locked door of his cell. He began to pace back and forth in the small room.

What could he do? If he sold the house to pay back his debt, his children would have no home. If he did not sell it, he would have to remain in prison until someone would pay the debt for him. Perhaps it would never be paid. And if he were not home to care for the crops, how could Ethan manage them alone?

There seemed to be no way for Mr. Rouzy to get out of jail and to pay the debt. What would become of his dear wife and children?

Things looked bad for his family.

A few days later, Mr. Rouzy heard footsteps approaching his cell. He looked up. His wife and his son Ethan had been given permission to visit. Mr. Rouzy could see that Ethan had something on his mind.

"Father," Ethan said. "Could it be that General Washington doesn't know what his agent has done? Mother and I think that could be possible."

Mr. Rouzy was silent a moment, his brow wrinkled in thought. Then his expression lightened. "Son," he said slowly. "It may well be that you and your mother are right. I have been feeling so bad that I haven't been able to think clearly. But being President of our new country is a big job. Perhaps General Washington has left some tasks in the hands of his agents, thinking they would conduct those tasks in the same way he himself would."

Ethan nodded and Mrs. Rouzy said, "We thought that if you could write to General Washington and—"

"A letter! Yes! Yes, of course!" exclaimed Mr. Rouzy. "If I had pen, ink, and paper, I would write to General Washington."

Mrs. Rouzy smiled. "We brought them, Reuben," she said. She gave him ink, a quill pen, a penknife to sharpen the quill, several sheets of paper, and a stick of sealing wax.

He looked at her and Ethan proudly. "My dear wife," he said. "You and our son have thought of everything."

Mr. Rouzy sat down at a small table and carefully wrote the

letter while his wife and son watched. When he had finished, he read the letter to them.

February 5, 1791

To His Excellency General George Washington
President of the United States of America
Philadelphia, Pennsylvania

Honored Sir:

I take my pen in hand to inform your Excellency that your agent here in Virginia has caused me to be thrown into jail because I did not have sufficient monies to repay the loan of one thousand pounds you so kindly made me. I had expected to be able to repay it before very long but I cannot do it at this time without impoverishing myself and my family.

General Washington, can it be that you do not know of the action your agent has taken against me? Your Excellency has done so many good Acts, this does not seem to be in accord.

I am writing to beg you to grant me another year in which to repay the loan. I feel quite certain that I shall be able to repay you in that time.

I sign myself humbly,
Your most obedient servant,
Reuben Rouzy

"Oh, Father," cried Ethan, his eyes shining. "That is a fine letter!"

"Yes," said Mrs. Rouzy. "Truly, it is."

Mr. Rouzy folded the paper and wrote the President's name and address on the outside. Mrs. Rouzy then held the stick of sealing wax over a candle. She let a drop of wax fall on the edge of the paper. Before the soft wax could harden, her husband pressed his seal ring against the wax, making an imprint. No one could open the letter now without breaking the seal.

"Ethan and I will take it to the postmaster," his wife said.

"Let us pray to God that it travels to General Washington safely, and that we are right about his not knowing," said Mr. Rouzy. He stood up, and the three of them bowed their heads in prayer.

Then came the waiting and wondering, hoping and fearing. Mr. Rouzy paced the floor again, but now he was no longer so sad. He thought of the many noble deeds of General Washington, and hoped that Washington would read the letter and give him the extra time he needed to repay the money.

Then a new thought came to Mr. Rouzy. What if the letter never reached General Washington? There were many ways for a letter to become lost. Postriders had to carry the mail on horseback, alone, through dangerous and difficult country. Sometimes letters blew away, or were delivered to the wrong person. There had been many cases of mail robberies. Postriders sometimes met with accidents. Mr. Rouzy remembered hearing rumors of a new Indian uprising in Pennsylvania. Maybe the postrider carrying his letter would be killed by Indians.

And as the days passed, Mr. Rouzy grew more worried. Why hadn't General Washington answered his letter? Mr. Rouzy was sure something had happened, and that Washington had never received the letter. Now he would have to stay in jail, and the debt would never be paid.

Then one day his wife and son came to see him again. This time they had a letter from the President. Mr. Rouzy's letter had reached General Washington! And Washington had answered it! They all waited anxiously for Mr. Rouzy to open the letter and read it.

It contained an order to the jailer for Mr. Rouzy's immediate release. There was also a note to Mr. Rouzy.

The note read, "You no longer owe me anything. The debt is hereby discharged. I am very sorry that this has happened. I am writing my agent severely reprimanding him for his action."

It was signed by President Washington himself.

Mr. Rouzy was free.

That evening at the Rouzy home the family gave thanks not only for their father's release from jail but for their renewed faith in their "beloved General Washington."

Bust of
George Washington
by Thomas Crawford

George Washington not only was a great man and a great leader, but also he was a generous and an understanding man, as this story points out.

Although he was wealthy, Washington had a deep love for his fellow Americans, rich and poor alike. He understood the problems of farmers like Reuben Rouzy because he had grown up on a farm himself.

Because of his greatness as a leader and as a man, it was said of George Washington that he was, "First in war, first in peace, and first in the hearts of his countrymen."

Some Other Books To Read

George Washington by Ingri M. and Edgar P. d'Aulaire. Published by Doubleday and Company, Inc., New York, 1936.

George Washington; an Initial Biography by Genevieve Foster. Published by Charles Scribner's Sons, New York, 1949.

George Washington, Leader of the People by Clara Ingram Judson. Published by Follett Publishing Company, Chicago, 1951.

Washington's America by Robin McKown. Published by Grosset and Dunlap, Inc., New York, 1961.

A
TEST
OF
COURAGE

Nachi, Chief of the Chiricahua Apaches, sat in council with some young braves.

"Men of the Rising Sun," he said. "My son, Cheis, wishes to take his test, young as he is. What do you say?"

Cheis waited eagerly for their answer. Like all Apache boys, he must spend two weeks alone in the wilderness, relying on his own wits to keep himself alive. Only then could he become a warrior in his tribe.

From their Chief's tone, the braves believed he wanted them to discourage the boy.

"It will be cold on the mountaintops at night," said one. "My answer is no!"

Cheis did not speak. He knew he would not wear enough clothing to protect him from the cold winds.

"You will be thirsty," said another. "You may carry no water. I say no!"

Still Cheis said nothing. He knew that much of the land over which he must travel was dry desert.

"You will have to find your own food," said a third brave. "You may take nothing to eat. I, too, say no!"

"I am an Apache," Cheis said proudly. "I do not fear thirst or hunger. Have I not trained with the boys of our tribe to go for two suns without food or water, or even sleep?"

"True," said Klosen, the last of the group. "But there are dangerous beasts in the wilderness. You would be frightened if you met a mountain lion with none of the tribe to protect you."

Cheis' black eyes flashed with anger.

"I shall not be afraid. I hope I do meet a mountain lion. I will kill it and bring its hide back to the camp of our people."

By Enid Johnson

Klosen sneered. He had always been jealous of Cheis. Several times he had missed deer that Cheis had later killed. He hoped Cheis *would* be allowed to go, that he would fail his test, and come running back to the safety of the stronghold before the two weeks had passed.

"What say you, Klosen?" the Chief asked. "Shall we let him go?"

"*Enju* (yes), Chief Nachi!" Klosen cried. "Let him prove himself brave enough to be a warrior with the Men of the Rising Sun!"

Cheis looked at the other braves. There was such longing in his eyes that they were moved to change their minds. One after another, each spoke the word Cheis wanted to hear, *"Enju!"*

"While you are in the wilderness, you must find your medicine," the Chief said.

Cheis knew what that meant. Every Apache boy must lie in a quiet place to receive his dream. The Apaches believed that whatever creature he dreamed of during his testing time would be his "medicine"—his guardian through all his life.

"I know, my father," Cheis answered.

"It is well," Chief Nachi said. "You may go."

Proud and happy, Cheis prepared for his journey. He made a bow, some arrows, a knife, and a spear.

Early one morning he went to see his mother.

"May we live to see each other again, my mother," Cheis said. This was the Apache way of saying good-by.

Then he ran up the mountainside, which rose straight from the camp. He was lucky that first afternoon. He found a small trickle of water in a hidden canyon. He drank as much as he could hold. But that night he did not look for food. Apaches believed a boy must go without eating to make his medicine come to him.

It was cold, and Cheis was almost naked. But like a true Apache, he never thought of discomfort. The only warning that he remembered was Klosen's dare. He must look for a mountain lion to prove to Klosen that he did not fear dangerous beasts.

But first he must find his medicine.

Shortly before dawn, after running much of the night, he lay down to sleep. He dreamed he was leading a band of his tribesmen. They were just about to be attacked by their enemies when the scream of an eagle warned them of danger.

Cheis awoke in great excitement. *An eagle was his medicine!*

When the sun rose, he left his resting place. Now he must make his lucky charm, which he would wear for the rest of his life.

From a tree, which had been struck by lightning, he took a piece of wood just the right size. He climbed to the top of the highest cliff. Seated on the bare ground, he carved the figure of an eagle with outspread wings. He cut a hole in the figure and tied it around his neck with buckskin string.

Now that he had received his medicine and carved his lucky charm, he could eat. How hungry he was! His stomach felt hollow, and his mouth was dry with thirst.

On that bare mountaintop there was no sign of water or food. He had traveled a long way from the canyon where there had been a trickle of water. Where could he find more?

Far down the steep mountain, he saw what looked like the bed of a stream. But when he reached the place, he found that the stream had dried out. Under a mesquite tree Cheis dug a hole with his hand. Soon his finger tips felt damp. He dug deeper until he made a small basin into which a little water began to seep.

He found a pile of leaves and twigs which he knew was a pack-rats' nest. With a stout branch from the mesquite tree, he beat on the nest until a few frightened pack rats scurried out.

Using the branch as a club, Cheis killed several of the little animals. He was about to pick them up when he was startled by a rattling sound. It was the sound a rattlesnake makes just before it strikes. There, a few inches from his hand, lay a huge rattlesnake, coiled and ready to strike!

Cheis pulled away too late. He felt a sharp pain on the back of his hand. The snake slithered away.

He wound more of his buckskin string tightly around the wrist of his bitten hand. Catching a live pack rat, he cut a slit in its side and put the bleeding little creature against his wound. The warmth of the animal's body drew out some of the deadly poison.

When that pack rat died, Cheis caught a second pack rat. One after another, he put five little animals against his snake bite. The last one did not die, so Cheis knew that the poison was all drawn out. Of course, his hand felt stiff and sore, but such things never bother an Apache!

All this excitement made him thirstier than ever. He went back to the hole he had dug and discovered almost a cup of water in it. Through a hollow reed, Cheis sucked the water into his mouth. Never had a drink of water tasted so good!

He started a small blaze with the twigs of the pack-rats' nest. Then he found some more pack rats. He cooked them and ate their flesh hungrily.

Before Cheis lay down to sleep that night, he said to himself, I have found my medicine and carved my lucky charm. Tomorrow I shall hunt for a mountain lion.

But day followed day, and Cheis saw no mountain lion. Often he was hungry. More often he was thirsty. He was wandering in a desert where nothing but cactus plants grew.

Far away against the sky, he saw a mountain range. He must reach those mountains, he thought, for there he would surely find water and food.

Even more important, he hoped to find tracks of a mountain lion. Cheis knew how Klosen would tease him if he returned to the stronghold without a mountain lion's hide!

He was able to drink some juice from a barrel cactus plant, but he was very hungry.

After a time, he came to a place where oak trees grew. Under the trees were some acorns. Although they were not ripe, they were better than nothing for the hungry boy. He put more of the acorns into the bottom of his arrow pouch to eat later on.

Once again, he caught sight of the mountains and trotted off towards them. All the time he kept looking for signs of a mountain lion.

In the clear air the mountains seemed nearer than they really were. It took him several days to reach the foothills. By this time, his hunger and thirst were almost unbearable.

But when he reached the wooded slopes of the mountains, he was rewarded. There on the ground were deer tracks! How good fresh deer meat would taste! He had had no meat since his meal of pack rats many days before.

Cheis knew how to lure a deer by blowing on a leaf held against his lips. "Whee! Wheee!" came the sound from his leaf whistle. Soon a fine, fat deer came into sight.

He fitted an arrow to his bow. With one shot he killed the deer. After skinning it, he cut some pieces from the carcass. He cooked the deer meat in the blaze of the fire he made.

With his hunger satisfied, he cooked more deer meat to take with him. Wrapping it in leaves, he fastened the bundle to his waist with his buckskin string.

"Now I will have enough food to last until I get back to the camp of my people," he told himself.

To keep track of the time, Cheis had cut a notch on his spear stalk every morning. He saw he had only three more days to stay. He had seen no mountain lion yet. He could not bear to face Klosen without a lion's hide!

But he had far to travel, so he must start back.

Soon the woods gave way to a stretch of sandy soil. What were those marks in the sand? They were much too large for deer tracks. Were they—*could* they be—the footprints of a mountain lion? They were!

He followed the tracks to the bank of a small river. Here was plenty of water, but Cheis was too excited to take more than just a few sips.

The tracks stopped at the river's edge. Cheis knew no mountain lion would go into water. Was it hiding somewhere in a cave? Surely, he had not found the tracks only to lose them!

A cottonwood tree stretched across the river. Cheis climbed out on a limb to see the surrounding country. He was wise enough to prop his bow and arrows against a nearby tree trunk.

Standing upright on the limb, he looked all around. There was no sign of the beast. But there were the tracks in the sand, plain as could be. Where could it be?

Suddenly, he heard the scream of an eagle flying overhead. Cheis looked up. There, on another branch a few feet above him, crouched a huge mountain lion! It was lashing its tail and tearing the bark of the tree with its great claws.

Cheis dropped down into the river. The lion sprang. It landed on the very place where Cheis had been standing.

Angry at losing its prey, the beast growled fiercely and clawed the bark harder than ever.

Cheis swam underwater the few feet to where he had left his bow and arrows. Aiming with great care, he let loose one of his arrows. It hit the lion. But Cheis was taking no chances. He knew how dangerous a wounded mountain lion could be! He sent a second arrow after the first.

The beast fell to the ground dead!

Cheis held his lucky charm in his hand. Now, he was sure that an eagle was truly his medicine. Just as the eagle in his dream had warned him of danger, so, too, had an eagle saved him this day.

He had proof to show Klosen that he was not afraid of dangerous beasts. He had met his test and proved he could take care of himself in the wilderness. He had found his medicine and made his lucky charm.

Now he was fit to take his place among the Men of the Rising Sun!

This is the story of a real person. Cheis later became "Cochise," the great Apache chief. He was friendly to the white men until he was betrayed by a young U. S. Army lieutenant. After this betrayal, when his beloved brother was hanged, Cochise vowed death to every white man he found.

For twelve years Cochise kept that vow. Then, through his friendship with Captain Thomas Jeffords, the only white man he ever trusted, Cochise made peace with his enemies.

Cochise kept the peace until his death in 1874. He was the greatest leader of the Apache nation.

Some Other Books To Read

The Apache Indians; Raiders of the Southwest by Sonia Bleeker. Published by William Morrow and Co., Inc., New York, 1951.

Cochise, Great Apache Chief by Enid Johnson. Published by Julian Messner, Inc., New York, 1953.

Cochise, Apache Warrior and Statesman by Edgar Wyatt. Published by McGraw-Hill Book Co., New York, 1953.

BIRD WOMAN AND FLAMING HAIR

By Clare Thorne

In the white man's books I am called Bird Woman. My real name is Sacagawea (Sak uh guh WEE uh).

When I was a girl, my people, the Shoshoni Indians, came down from the mountains every summer to camp on the buffalo plains. Our fathers hunted, and our mothers dried the meat so there would be food in our lodges the next winter.

One day, in my ninth year, a scout rode into camp to warn us that a war party of a hundred Minataree braves was coming up the riverbank. Our Shoshoni warriors laughed at the foolish enemy. Our braves were more than twice a hundred.

But the war party of Minatarees carried shining sticks that spoke lightning and thunder. I learned later that these sticks are called guns, and that the Minatarees got them from the white man. On that terrible morning, our hunters who were not killed rode back, shouting that the women and children must hide themselves. Everything was confusion. I ran toward the place where my elder brother, Black Bow, had gone to hide.

All at once I came to the bank of the river, and there, just below me, were four Minatarees on horses!

It was too late to hide myself. I tried to cross the river. But before I was halfway across, one of the Minatarees caught me. He seized my arm and pulled me up on his horse in front of him. He was Red Arrow, the Minataree, who took me with him all the way back to his village on the Big River that white men call the Missouri.

Red Arrow was a man of good heart. He and his wife were kind to me. They treated me like a daughter, but I was not happy in their lodge, which was made of mud like a prairie dog's home.

I passed many years in the village on the Big River. Then one night Red Arrow played the betting game with a white trader named Charbonneau. This was a man who did not speak with a straight tongue, and Red Arrow lost everything. Having lost all other things except his lodge, he used me as his bet, and he lost me, too. That is how I, Sacagawea, came to be the wife of Charbonneau, the trader.

Charbonneau was a boaster and of little courage, but he was father to the little son who was born to me. I tried to do all I could for his comfort. But more and more my heart longed for my home in the mountains.

One day there came to the village of Earth Houses some white men. They were sent by their Great White Chief to find the trail west, across the plains, over the high mountains, and to the Everywhere-Salt-Water. They asked the Minatarees for guides who could show them the trail and who could trade with my people, the Shoshoni. My people, the Shoshoni, owned many horses, and the Americans needed horses to cross the mountains.

My man, Charbonneau, offered to be their guide. For once I was glad. I thought, now I will take my little son in my blanket and follow the Big River to its roots in my mountains. Once we are with my people, the Shoshoni, they will buy our freedom, and we will remain with them forever.

There were two white chiefs. The tall one was named Lewis, but the Minatarees called him Long Knife. The young one had hair the color of a woodfire. His name was Clark, but I called him Flaming Hair.

Soon we started up the Big River. We had thirty-three people in two large boats and six small boats. As we approached my mountains, I grew impatient at our slowness. One day I spoke of it.

Long Knife was impatient, too. "Before long, heavy rains will fall in the mountains," he said. "If we do not find your people and buy horses, it will be too late. We will have to turn back."

"And if we do that?" I asked.

"We will not take this trail again."

That night I prayed to my mountain gods not to close the way they had opened to Sacagawea, but to show me the trail to my people, the Shoshoni. Next morning, I saw smoke on the side of the mountain ahead of us.

It was a sign. Shoshoni scouts had seen us. They were calling my people together. They would lie in wait and destroy us. There was no time to lose now.

"We must run up the trail quickly, before the Shoshoni have gathered!" I told Flaming Hair.

"You can't run, Bird Woman. Not with the baby in your blanket," he said to me.

"We can't go now anyway," said Charbonneau. "There's a storm coming. We must wait till it passes."

But I would not listen to either of them. I started up the trail, holding my blanket tight around me so that my little son rode on my back like a hunter on his pony. Flaming Hair and Charbonneau followed. Before we had come to the foot of the mountain, the first drops of rain fell.

Charbonneau shouted that we must turn back and seek shelter. Flaming Hair saw a cave on the side of the dry riverbed, and we all ran to it. There we were safe in a fine dry place, or so we thought at first. But the rain kept falling.

Soon Charbonneau was grumbling louder than ever, "If this keeps up, there will be a flood down the riverbed."

For once he spoke truth. In my mountains there are floods that come like a wall of water. As we listened, we could already hear a deep rumbling sound.

"We must not wait here," I told Flaming Hair. "The water wall may soon reach the mouth of this cave."

"All right, let's run for it! Down the riverbed and up the far side! That's easier!"

I started, but I slipped and fell.

It was Flaming Hair who helped me and my little son all the way down the riverbed and across the stream that had already formed at the bottom. Then he started up the far side, pulling me after him. In our ears was the roar of the water coming. If we fell, it would be to death on the rocks below. If we climbed too slowly, the wall of water would reach up and snatch us.

But Flaming Hair did not stop. Once the young tree he was holding came loose at the roots. I would have let go so as not to drag him down with us, but he held my wrist and found another tree to pull up by. At last, we reached safety on a wide ledge, high above the water.

I could not speak my thanks to Flaming Hair, but in my heart I made a promise I would help him in something as big as what he had done for us.

As we followed the trail up the mountain, I heard the beating of horses' hoofs.

"Stand back and let me be the one to greet whoever is riding down on us," I said.

Flaming Hair and Charbonneau hid themselves in the brush at the side of the trail, and I stood alone, facing the riders.

"My people, my brothers!" I called as soon as I could see them. "Do not shoot your arrows! It is I—Sacagawea—your sister, long lost to you!"

They reined in their horses, and looked down at me.

"Sacagawea?" they said softly. "Yes, it is you."

They took me to my brother, Black Bow. He was now chief of the Shoshoni.

I called to Flaming Hair and Charbonneau. A runner was sent to bring Long Knife and the rest. When they had come, I spoke for both sides.

Long Knife asked if our people knew the trail to the Everywhere-Salt-Water. Black Bow told him the way.

Long Knife asked them if Black Bow would sell horses to the white chiefs. Black Bow said to tell him that our people had few horses to spare, but they would take counsel of the other Shoshoni tribes and give an answer the next day.

That night I sat in the lodge of my brother, and he told me of all that had happened to our people since I, Sacagawea, had been captured.

"We starve, Younger Sister. The plains are dark with buffalo. But we dare not hunt there because the plains tribes kill our people with the white man's shining sticks. We die of hunger here in the mountains. I have sent messages to all the Shoshoni tribes."

"What messages?" I asked him.

"To come and help us kill these white chiefs."

"Brother!" I cried. "They have done you no evil. Why should you kill them?"

"Our people die for lack of the shining sticks. Your chiefs carry them. Either they die or we must."

I was angry, and that gave me courage to speak against my brother. "By killing the white chiefs you will not feed our people. After one fight with the plains tribes, you will have no more of the guns' food. Be wise, O my brother," I begged him. "Be friends with the white chiefs. They are as straight as the straightest pine tree."

"Very well," he said. "We will sell them horses and buy your freedom."

My freedom! How long I had dreamed of it, and of living with my little son in the lodge of my brother! But without me the white chiefs would never find their trail's end. I told this to Black Bow.

"What is that to you, Sacagawea? What if they do not find the Everywhere-Salt-Water?"

"I have made a promise," I told him. "I have promised to help Flaming Hair, who saved me and my little son. When I have done that, I will be free to return to my people."

So it was that I went with the white chiefs all the way to the Everywhere-Salt-Water, to the place where angry waves rush on the shore even when no wind blows.

I fulfilled my secret promise to help Flaming Hair.

Today, in the city of Helena, Montana, there is a statue of Sacagawea, Long Knife, and Flaming Hair. It stands in memory of the help the Indian girl gave to her friends, Meriwether Lewis (Long Knife) and William Clark (Flaming Hair).

It was because of Sacagawea's help that Lewis and Clark were able to blaze a new trail across the West to the Pacific Ocean. Their journey started a new era of trading in the western territories. Their records gave us important information about the ways of the Indian tribes they met along the way.

After Sacagawea had guided Long Knife and Flaming Hair to the Everywhere-Salt-Water, which we call the Pacific Ocean, she returned to her mountains in search of her Shoshoni people. It was many years before she was able to find them again. By that time, her little son had grown to manhood. Clark had seen to it that Sacagawea's son was educated in the white man's schools. It was Clark's way of showing his thanks for the help Sacagawea had given to him and to his friends.

The Pacific Ocean at the mouth of the Columbia River on the Washington-Oregon border ▶

Some Other Books To Read

Winged Moccasins; The Story of Sacajawea by Frances J. Farnsworth. Published by Julian Messner, Inc., New York, 1954.

Trails West and Men Who Made Them by Edith Dorian and W. N. Wilson. Published by McGraw-Hill Book Co., New York, 1955.

Sacajawea: Guide of Lewis and Clark by Jerry Siebert. Published by Houghton Mifflin Co., Boston, 1960.

THE
DISAPPEARANCE
OF
BLACK RAVEN

By Robert M. Savage

The tall boy raced his horse through the forest. His two Indian friends were close behind. They were racing from the river to the chief's wigwam. The boy was not an Indian, but he was dressed just like a young brave. He was called "Black Raven," a name the chief had given him.

He knew the chief would be waiting to greet the winner. This time, he did not look forward to seeing the chief whom he loved like a father. Today he must tell the chief that he wanted to go home.

It was not going to be easy. The chief and all the Cherokees had been good to him. The boy had run away from home to live with the Cherokees, and they had welcomed him as one of their own. They had taught him things about the forest and about the river that few white men would ever know.

Black Raven reached the edge of the forest and turned down the path that led to the Cherokee camp. He urged his horse to go faster. He could see the chief waiting to greet the winner.

The two Indian boys tried to catch him, but their horses could not match the long, graceful strides of Black Raven's horse.

As his horse galloped through the Cherokee camp, Black Raven waved to the Indians who had gathered to watch the race. They nodded their heads in approval of the way he handled his horse.

When he reached the chief's wigwam, the boy reined his horse to a stop and leaped from its back.

The chief came forward. "Black Raven rides faster than the wind," he said. "He rides faster than his Cherokee friends!"

"I have won only because I have a faster horse," the boy said in the Cherokee language.

The other two riders thundered into camp, stopping in front of the chief's wigwam. They slid from their horses and ran to the boy and the chief.

"Black Raven has learned to handle a horse better than his friends," the chief insisted. "He has learned how to play the Cherokee games so that he is always the winner."

The boy did not want his friends to be jealous of him. "The chief praises me too much before my friends," he said.

A tender smile creased the chief's face.

"Black Raven is quiet today," one of the braves sneered. "Something troubles him—something bad."

Black Raven turned away. Now he knew that his friends were angry because he had won the race. They wanted to make trouble for him with the chief, and this made him unhappy.

The chief commanded the young braves to leave. Grumbling, they led their horses away.

"What is troubling you, Black Raven?" the chief asked.

The boy could not tell of his plan to leave, not right now. Later, after they ate and the council fire was lighted, he would tell.

That evening, Black Raven watched from the shadows as the men sat around the council fire. He listened to their stories about Cherokee braves. He knew that before going to sleep he must tell the chief that he had made up his mind to leave.

When the story telling was finished, the braves walked off to their huts. Only the chief remained. Black Raven stepped from the shadows into the light of the dying fire. He took a deep breath.

"I have something important to tell you," he said to the chief.

The chief smiled and motioned the boy closer to the fire. "I also have something important to tell Black Raven."

The chief broke a twig in two pieces, one longer than the other. The boy knew that the chief was making a game. Whoever drew the long twig must speak first. Black Raven hoped that the chief would be the one to speak first. He reached to draw one of the twigs. He drew the short one.

"Listen carefully," the chief began. "In the time that you have lived with the Cherokees, you have proved that you are brave and fair. You run with the speed of a deer and ride better than any young brave in camp. Your eyes are clear, and your hands are steady."

The chief paused and looked straight into Black Raven's eyes. "The chief has no son. Now he would like to make Black Raven his son forever. I want to adopt you as my own."

The boy's real father had died many years ago. Now the chief was honoring him in a way that he had not honored anyone before. This was the boy's chance to be known among Cherokees everywhere as the son of the brave and honorable chief.

The chief leaned forward and smiled again. "Black Raven does not have to give me his answer now. You can tell me when the sun rises on another day. Now, what is the important thing you wanted to say to me?"

The boy did not know what to say. Tomorrow he planned to leave, to go home. "I will talk about it when the sun rises on another day," he finally answered.

When the boy fell asleep, he dreamed that his mother was calling to him, begging him to come home. He felt sorry that he had run away. He wanted to go home. But how could he leave, now that the chief had offered to adopt him? How could he explain to the chief that he wanted to leave?

Black Raven was awakened in the morning by the excited shouts of his friends.

"The good news has been made known," they cried. "Everyone knows the high honor the chief has placed upon you! Now you will truly be one of us! Now we will not be angry when you win. You will be the chief's son!"

"Who told you this?" Black Raven asked.

"The old squaw who knows everything!" they answered.

Black Raven rushed past his friends. He did not look toward the chief's wigwam as he ran into the forest.

He had to think and to make a decision before he could go back to camp. He knew he must return home to his mother. Yet, how could he disappoint the chief who had been like a father to

him, and who now wanted to be his real father? He loved the
chief and he loved his mother, too. He could not have them both.

He thought and thought, first deciding one way, and then the
other. All day long he roamed the forest that he had come to
know so well. Toward evening he built a fire and lay down beside it. He looked at the trees and at the sights he had learned
to love. He listened to the sounds of the birds and the bubbling
brooks.

What should I do, he wondered. What should I do?

As the sun dropped below the treetops, he fell asleep without
having made up his mind.

When Black Raven did not return all that day, the chief
started to worry. Black Raven had never gone off before without
telling where he was going and when he would return.

Darkness came and the council fire was lighted. The chief's
worry deepened. What if something had happened to the boy?
Finally, he asked for Black Raven's horse.

"What is wrong?" the chief's wife asked. "It is late—"

The chief mounted the horse. "I will go to look for my son!"
he said.

He let the horse lead the way into the dark forest. The

horse knew Black Raven's favorite places.

The moon kept climbing higher in the night sky, but there was no sign of the boy anywhere. The chief became discouraged.

He turned the horse to return to camp. But suddenly the chief smelled something. It was smoke from a recent fire! It came from a spot so thick with trees and shrubbery that it would be impossible to lead the horse into it. Dismounting, the chief crept into the thicket.

He found the boy fast asleep in a small clearing.

"Black Raven," he called quietly. "My son—"

The boy awoke instantly, ready to leap.

"Do not be frightened. It is the chief, your father."

"Why did you come looking for me?" the boy asked.

"Something troubles you, my son. It is not like you to leave without a word. Now that I have found you, it is time for you to tell me what troubles you."

"I can't!" the boy cried. "How can I hurt you? You have been so good to me!"

The wise chief put his hands on the boy's shoulders. "In your heart there is a longing to see your own people. In your heart you want to leave, but you do not want to hurt me by telling me so. You must do what you think you should do. You are no prisoner here.

"Go," the chief said. "Go with your father's blessing. You have learned much in your stay with the Cherokee. You have learned of the beauty of the skies and the creatures that fly in it. You have learned of the beauty of the forest and the creatures that roam in it. You have washed your face in the rain and listened to the wind. You have learned that there can be friendship between the white man and the Cherokee.

"These things you will never forget. These things will call you back to me whenever you are troubled, whenever your heart is sad. Go now and the chief's heavy heart will be made glad because he knows that one day Black Raven will return!"

The boy called Black Raven was Sam Houston. This story took place in 1811 when Sam was eighteen years old. When he grew up, Sam became the commander in chief of the Texas army. Under his brave leadership, the army of Texas defeated the army of Mexico, and Texas became an independent nation. Through Sam Houston's efforts, Texas later became part of the United States.

The chief's words that day came true. Often when Sam was troubled, he went back to eastern Tennessee to live with his Cherokee friends. The chief, whose name was Oolooteka, remained Sam's friend and helped keep peace between the Cherokee and the white man.

Oolooteka

Sam Houston

Some Other Books To Read

Six Feet Six: The Heroic Story of Sam Houston by Bessie R. and Marquis Adams. Published by the Bobbs-Merrill Company, Inc., Indianapolis, 1931.

Sam Houston, the Tallest Texan by William Johnson. Published by Random House, New York, 1953.

Profiles in Courage. Young Readers' Edition by John F. Kennedy. Published by Harper & Brothers, New York, 1961.

The Prisoners Are Loose

By Virginia Barrett Novinger

David awoke from a deep sleep. He could hear the slap, slap of the water against the wooden sides of the *Essex,* a ship in the United States Navy. His hammock swayed gently as the *Essex* knifed its way through the waters of the Atlantic Ocean.

But there was something else he could hear, something strange. Was it someone breathing? Someone standing close to him? Yes, that was it!

He lay, not opening his eyes, trying to breathe evenly. There it was again—a quick intake of breath, a slight shuffling of feet. David still kept his eyes shut.

Something was wrong! He knew it! Knowing the room was as dark as the night outside, David dared open his eyes to tiny slits. Sure enough a big man was bending over him. He had a large knife in his hand.

The man's knees were flexed and his shoulders were hunched as if he were about to spring. A small shaft of light from the door outlined the man's form and sent silvery beams from the edge of his knife.

David recognized the man as a crew member of the British man-of-war, *Alert.* David had had his first taste of battle the day before when the *Essex* had fought the *Alert* along the Atlantic Coast. The *Essex* had won the battle and had captured the crew of the *Alert.* The crew of the *Alert* were prisoners on the *Essex.* They were now supposed to be locked securely below deck.

David again shut his eyes tightly, pacing his breathing to make it seem as though he were asleep.

If he finds out I'm awake, he'll surely kill me, David thought. What can he be up to?

David was eleven years old. He was the youngest midshipman in the United States Navy.

And here he lay with a dangerous man not more than a breath away from him, holding a knife at his throat!

And then, thinking that no one was awake, the man left the room. His feet made no sound. But a soft moving current of air told David the man had gone.

David opened his eyes cautiously. The other midshipmen in the room were asleep. He slipped out of his hammock and moved quietly on stocking feet to the door, which the prisoner had not closed.

I've got to tell Captain Porter, David thought. If one prisoner is loose, the rest of them must be, too! And I'm sure they are up to no good.

David waited a moment outside the door of the room. He peered into the darkness on all sides of him. Then he moved silently, quiet as a moth, quick as a fly, down the berth deck to the Captain's cabin.

Once inside Captain Porter's room, David began to wonder if he had imagined the whole thing.

Maybe it was a dream, he thought. If it was a dream, Captain Porter will be angry with me.

Captain Porter not only was skipper of the *Essex,* but also he was David's foster father. David especially wanted the Captain to be proud of him. He didn't want to make any mistakes. The *Essex* was a fine ship. Yesterday when they had captured the *Alert,* the British man-of-war with twenty guns, Captain Porter had been proud of his whole crew. And now David had to be very sure that he wasn't making up the story.

But then he remembered the gleam of the knife and the hot breath of the sailor who had stood over him. David knew that it had not been a dream.

He hesitated only a moment more, listening to the Captain's loud snoring.

"Captain Porter!" he whispered, shaking the sleeping man.

Captain Porter snorted and turned to his other side muttering something David didn't understand.

"Captain Porter, sir," David continued, shaking him again. "The prisoners are loose! Wake up! Wake up, sir!"

The Captain opened his eyes, looked about for a moment, and then swung his feet to the floor. He listened intently to David's story while tugging at his boots.

"Follow me!" he called to David over his shoulder as he ran for the deck in great strides.

"Fire! Fire!" yelled the Captain, his hands cupped to carry his words. "All hands on deck! Take your fire stations!"

For a moment David wondered if the Captain had lost his senses. There wasn't any fire. Fire was the thing to be feared most on a wooden ship. But it certainly wasn't anything to joke about. Surely Captain Porter wasn't joking now!

Then David realized what the Captain was doing. For days and days at sea, with no activity to keep the crew busy, the Captain had drilled his men in the proper way to put out a fire. Any time of the day or night the Captain might call for a fire drill.

At the shout of "Fire!" every man on board sprang from his hammock, grabbed his cutlass and blanket, and ran for his post. If his clothes caught on fire, a sailor was to roll himself in his blanket to put out the flames. His cutlass, the sharp pointed knife every sailor carried, would be needed if he jumped overboard and had to fight off sharks, or if he had to cut his way

through flaming sail or rope.

"Man your posts!" shouted the Captain. "Fire in the hold!"

Essex sailors darted this way and that, scurrying to their posts. They were well drilled and knew exactly where they were to go.

David tried to stay out of their way but he could not find a spot to stand where some sailor, knife in teeth, blanket draped about him, would not brush against him.

I'll stay right near the Captain, maybe he'll need me, David decided.

The prisoners from the *Alert* were completely confused. They didn't know what to do. They were terrified of the fire they thought was raging in the hold. They scurried out of the lower regions of the ship and rushed to the deck. They screamed in terror, running about in panic.

"Help us!" they pleaded.

"Get us off this cursed ship!" they cried, running this way and that way.

Then Captain Porter shouted another order, "Grab them, men!" Immediately the *Essex* crewmen sprang into action. Before long, most of the prisoners were captured again.

The leader of the *Alert's* crew tried to leap over the rail of the ship. One of the *Essex* crewmen pulled him back.

"Ahoy, there, my fine fellow," cried the *Essex* crewman. "And just where do you think you're goin'? The sharks will be glad to see you, I'm sure, but we'll just keep you here for a while before we toss you overboard."

"Oh, no, don't throw me to the sharks," begged the man. "Just put out the fire that's raging in the hold."

"Fire under control!" roared Captain Porter when he saw that his men had captured every *Alert* crew member.

"Let's get this gang of cutthroats below again," he shouted loudly.

As they were being herded below, the *Alert* crew realized that they had been tricked. They mumbled and grumbled, but it was too late for them to do anything about it. This time the door was locked securely behind them, and a stout chain put across it for good measure.

When all of the prisoners were locked up again, Captain Porter called David into his cabin.

David's hat was much too big for him, and it slipped down over his forehead a little. He tried to stand up straight before the Captain. He threw his shoulders back and turned his toes outward in the best sailor fashion. He wanted to make Captain Porter proud of him.

And then he heard the Captain speaking, "There would have been some blood shed tonight, David, if you had not used your head.

"You might have run into other prisoners on the berth deck, boy. Some of your own blood might have been spilled. Did you think of that?" The Captain's voice shook just a little.

"Well, sir, yes I did, sir," David admitted. "But I looked all around me, and there was no one there, so I just ran, sir," he finished.

"The *Essex* is grateful to you, Midshipman David Farragut," Captain Porter said. "I am proud to call you midshipman. And prouder still to say that you are my son!"

This incident happened on a night in August, 1812, during the War of 1812.

Captain Porter glowed with pride for this boy, David Glasgow Farragut, who at so young an age had distinguished himself in his service to the United States Navy. David Farragut became one of the greatest naval officers in early American history. During the Civil War he fought for the North and gained the nickname of "Old Salamander," because of his ability to sail his boats under heavy gunfire.

In 1866, Congress made him the first admiral of the United States Navy.

If you would like to read more about this famous American naval hero, you can find some exciting stories about him in the books listed below.

Some Other Books To Read

David Farragut, Sea Fighter by Marie Mudra. Published by Julian Messner, Inc., New York, 1953.

And Long Remember; Some Great Americans Who Have Helped Me by Dorothy Canfield Fisher. Published by McGraw-Hill Book Co., Inc., New York, 1959.

"I WILL PROTECT IT WITH MY LIFE"

By Audrey J. Schuster

The wagon clattered across the bridge and came to a halt. Ahead, a narrow, dusty road followed the curve of the river. On the left, woods sprinkled with the gold and rust colors of late summer stretched across the Virginia countryside. The young driver, Stephen Pleasanton, touched the reins and the wagon lurched forward. He would follow the road for awhile.

About two miles past the bridge, he came to an old, broken-down barn, which stood behind a hill. It was almost dusk, and he would soon need a place to stay for the night. The horse drew the wagon slowly over the hill and stopped before the barn.

Stephen thrust his hand into the wagon and searched until he found the bag containing the document. Stuffing the bag into his shirt, he smiled as he remembered Secretary James Monroe's words: "I'm entrusting you with the most important document of the United States. It was for this that our brave men fought and died during the Revolutionary War. The British must not get their hands on it."

Stephen had replied, "Mr. Secretary, I will protect this paper with my life."

Then he had left the city of Washington, D. C., hoping the British soldiers would not stop him and find the paper.

Well, no trouble so far, Stephen thought, as he unhitched the wagon and led the horse into the barn.

Inside the barn it was musty and dark except for a few slivers of light that came in through some cracks in the walls. All the stalls were empty. He stabled his horse and found a ladder leading to the hayloft.

He put his foot gingerly on the first rung. He hesitated for a moment before stepping up.

Crack! The sound exploded in the barn like a rifle shot. The rung split beneath his foot and he fell back. He jumped up quickly and turned around, but there was no one near to hear the noise.

He tried the ladder again, and the next rung held. Carefully, he climbed until he reached the loft. Some of the boards were missing and others were splintered, but he found a corner where he could lie down. At least he would be safe for the night.

And there he slept, dreaming about the important paper he carried.

The sunlight, pouring through the cracked roof, woke him early the next morning. He rose slowly, all his joints aching. I can't sleep like that for many more nights, he thought. Maybe the British have left Washington. Maybe I can go back to-night. Testing each step, he walked to the door of the loft and pushed it open. It creaked and the horse whinnied below.

Stephen yawned and peered out through the early morning haze. He could just make out the outskirts of Washington. The capital seemed engulfed in the smoky haze. But wait! It wasn't just haze that he saw. Smoke rose from where the government buildings should be.

"Great heavens!" he cried. "They're burning Washington!"

He hurried over the splintered boards, down the ladder, and out of the barn. He raced up the hill. From the top of the hill he could see the smoke billowing up over the city. It was much too close, he thought, as he ran back to get the horse. He must get away with his valuable paper. The British might be starting into the countryside already.

He harnessed the horse quickly and climbed into the wagon. Making sure the precious document was still in his shirt, he whipped the reins. The wagon rumbled down the road and rolled north.

Deep in thought as the wagon rolled across the Virginia countryside, Stephen was startled by a voice shouting at him.

"Halt! Where do you think you're going?"

A British officer walked onto the road toward the wagon as Stephen reined in his horse sharply.

Stephen glanced over the officer's shoulder and stared at the three soldiers following behind. What could he answer? He must protect the paper, even if he had to die for it.

"Well, speak up," demanded the officer.

"Sir," said Stephen meekly, "I'm just a poor peddler. I'm on my way back to Virginia to my wife and children."

"You should be off the roads," growled the officer. "There's a war on, you know."

"Oh, yes, sir. That's why I wanted to get back home quickly. I don't want my family to worry." Stephen held his breath.

The officer strode over to the wagon and looked in. He picked up one of the linen sacks and squeezed it. A puff of flour escaped. He dropped it, brushing his hands together briskly. Bending down, he peered underneath the old wagon.

Then he straightened up and looked at Stephen.

Stephen prayed that the officer wouldn't look inside his shirt.

"Well, you look harmless enough," the officer said. "Go on, but better keep to the back roads. Some other soldier might mistake you for a spy." The officer laughed at the thought.

Stephen murmured, "Yes, sir, thank you, sir," and clicked his teeth to the horse.

"Well, boy, almost caught, weren't we?" he said softly to the horse once they were out of sight. He snapped the reins and the horse quickened its pace.

He drove all day until he reached the outskirts of Leesburg. This was better, Stephen thought. Surely the British wouldn't march thirty miles into Virginia. But where could he stay until it was safe to return to Washington? Whom could he trust? He led the horse off the road behind some bushes. It would be easier to look over the town on foot.

He started walking, then stopped several yards from the first house he saw. Two boys were playing ball in the yard, while a small spotted dog scooted between them barking. Across a field some distance away, he saw the steeple of a church. A church is always a place of refuge, he thought, and he headed in that direction.

Next to the church was a large, whitewashed house. Tall shrubs enclosed the wide green lawn. There were no other houses nearby.

Stephen sat down in the shade of the shrubbery and tried to think of a story he could tell the minister. What reason could he give for coming to Leesburg and asking for shelter? Or should he tell the truth?

"All right now, what do you want?" shouted a voice behind him.

Stephen jumped at the voice and whirled around. He was looking into the barrel of a rifle. The minister was holding the rifle.

"I, why, I—" He tried to stand but the minister kept him pinned to the ground with the rifle. "I was just looking for a place to stay for the night," Stephen blurted out. "I'm on my way north to join my family."

The minister frowned. "Traveling kind of light, aren't you?" he asked.

"I had to leave Washington in a hurry . . . The British burned the city, you know."

"Yes, I heard," replied the minister. "But how do I know you're not a British spy?"

"A spy!" cried Stephen. For an instant his hand touched his shirt where he kept the paper. "But of course I'm not a spy," he protested.

The minister had noted the move. "Aha," he said triumphantly. "What do you have there? What are you hiding?"

Stephen tried to move back against the bushes, but the minister jabbed him with the gun. "Come on, take it out, slowly," he said.

Reluctantly, Stephen drew the bag with the paper in it from his shirt.

"Open it," the minister ordered.

"Sir, I assure you these are only some letters from my family," pleaded Stephen. "Just some personal—"

"Open it," said the minister. "I have some spies of my own, you see. I know how close the British are, and they're not going to stir up any trouble in Leesburg."

Slowly Stephen drew the parchment from the bag. He closed his eyes and prayed silently that the minister was as loyal as he sounded. If not, Stephen would have to try to disarm him. The document must not fall into British hands at any cost.

The minister took the document and read, "'In Congress, July 4, 1776. The unanimous Declaration of the thirteen . . . united States of America.'" He looked up sharply, then back at the parchment to make sure he was not mistaken. "The Declaration of Independence," he pronounced in a hushed voice. "But what are you doing with it?" he demanded.

Stephen straightened up as much as he could in his sitting position. "Sir, the Secretary of State entrusted the Declaration to me when he learned that the British were about to raid Washington. I am a clerk in his office." He added, "I have sworn to protect the Declaration with my life."

"Humph!" sniffed the minister. "Fine protector you are, getting yourself caught by an old man like me." He smiled down at the parchment in his hand. "But until the British have been driven out of our land, we will protect this with both our lives," he declared.

This is a true story of something that happened during the War of 1812 between the United States and Great Britain. Few remember Stephen Pleasanton or the minister whose name was Littlejohn. But what they did will be long remembered by the people of the United States. After Pleasanton's meeting with Littlejohn, the Declaration of Independence was hidden in the minister's home for several weeks. It was later returned to Washington after the British soldiers left the capital.

The Declaration of Independence remained in Washington until World War II, when it was sent secretly to Fort Knox, Kentucky.

Today the Declaration of Independence is back in Washington again. You can see it in the National Archives Building, where it lies in a sealed glass case filled with helium, which is expected to preserve it for as long as the United States endures.

The Declaration of Independence

Some Other Books To Read

Birthday of a Nation: July 4, 1776 by Frances Rogers and Alice Beard. Published by J. B. Lippincott Co., Philadelphia, 1945.

The Fourth of July Story by Alice Dalgliesh. Published by Charles Scribner's Sons, New York, 1956.

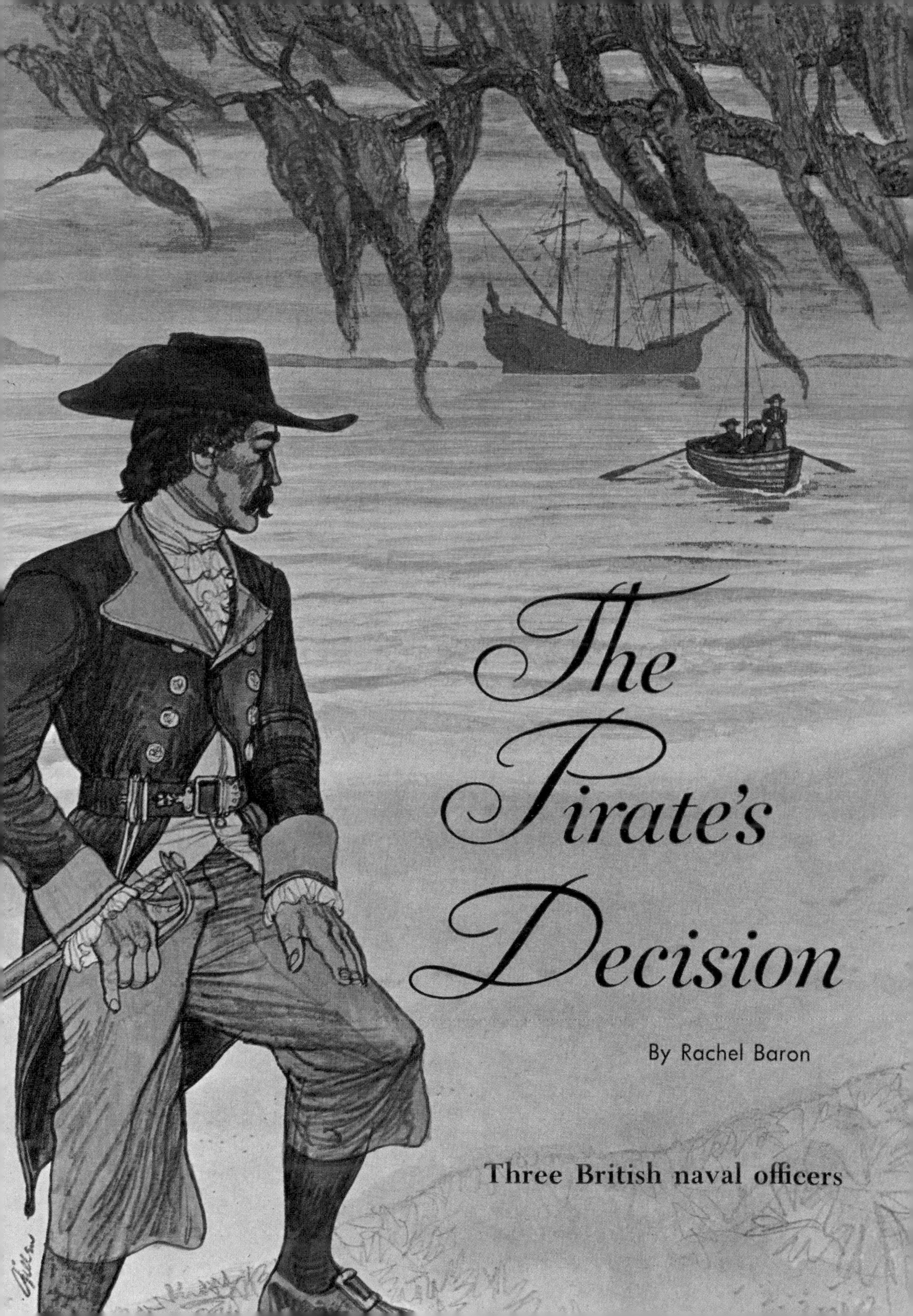

The Pirate's Decision

By Rachel Baron

Three British naval officers

rowed their tiny boat toward the Louisiana shore . . . .

In the dim light of early morning, they could barely make out the outline of the ship they had just left. They strained their eyes to stare toward shore. What they saw frightened them.

"Captain," said one of the officers. "There are men on shore. They look like pirates."

"Good," replied the captain. "That is why we have come here."

"But what if the pirates refuse our offer? We may be killed."

"That is the chance we must take."

The three Englishmen pulled their boat up on the shore. They tried to appear calm as they walked away from the boat. In an instant they were surrounded by pirates.

"Hello there!" shouted the captain. "We are officers of the British Royal Navy. We have come in friendship to see your leader."

"I am the leader," said one of the pirates. He stepped forward and bowed. "Welcome to Louisiana!" He smiled and his black eyes sparkled with suspicion.

The pirates moved in close to their leader, murmuring loudly.

The captain returned the bow and said, "I have with me the personal greetings of His Majesty, the King of England."

"You are most gracious," replied the pirate leader.

"We have some letters that we would like to have you read and consider." The captain held out a packet of letters tied together with a satin ribbon.

The pirate leader glanced quickly at the Englishmen and then at his own men. Then he raised his hand for silence. "These gentlemen must be tired after their long journey.

"My friends," he said to the British officers. "You must be hungry. Whatever business you have to discuss with me can wait until you have had something to eat. We shall dine together. After we eat, you may show me your letters. Come, gentlemen, put away those letters and follow me."

The band of pirates stood aside while their leader led his guests across the beach to his house. His home was built like a palace, large and elegant.

Inside his house, he brought the three Englishmen into his dining room. The great table was spread with expensive linen. There were plates made of heavy carved silver and goblets of the finest crystal.

As they feasted, a large clock in the corner of the dining room ticked away the minutes.

"We are impressed by your kindness," said the captain. "Such magnificence is fit for a king."

"Thank you!"

"But soon, we must show you the letters."

"Oh no, my friends," responded the pirate leader. "In Louisiana we never interrupt our meal by talking about business. The letters will come later."

They continued to eat. And the clock continued to tick.

Finally the servants came to clear the table. The pirate leader waited for the dishes to be removed. And then he settled back in the depths of a stuffed chair.

"All right, gentlemen," he said slowly. "You have completed your feast. Now, tell me why you have come to Louisiana."

The captain handed the packet of letters to his host. Silently, the pirate leader untied the satin ribbon and began to read the first letter.

The only sound was the ticking of the large clock.

The pirate leader read the letter slowly. The Englishmen watched in silence. They watched every expression on his face, every movement of his hands.

Finally he finished the letter and glanced up. The three Englishmen leaned forward in their chairs waiting for him to speak. What would he say? Would he accept their offer? Or would he turn his band of pirates against them?

But he said nothing. He looked at the letter again and began to read it a second time.

The three officers looked at one another but remained silent.

At last the pirate finished the letter and put it down. Again the Englishmen leaned forward. But the pirate leader picked up the second letter without saying a word.

He finished the second letter. Then he read the third and the fourth. When he finished reading the letters, he put them aside and sat in silence.

The Englishmen waited for him to speak, but he did not.

Finally the English captain spoke up.

"You are hesitating," he said. "Let me tell you in my own words why we have come to Louisiana to see you."

The pirate smiled coldly, and then he nodded.

"We have come as your friends," said the captain. "We ask that you be *our* friend. You rule over one thousand men. We know who your men are. We know that they come from many parts of the world—from Portugal, Spain, France, yes, even England. We ask that you join us to fight the American enemy. And if you do this, we will make you a captain. We will also give you thirty thousand dollars."

"Continue," said the pirate.

"You, sir, are a Frenchman by birth. And England and France are allies. So as a Frenchman, your place is with the English.

"We know that many Americans do not like you. We know, for instance, that some of your men have been jailed unjustly by the Americans. We also know that the Governor of Louisiana has posted a reward for your capture. So we know you will want to be our friend.

"You will gain riches through your association with us. Through your friendship with our side your fortune will be made."

The pirate smiled but said nothing. The only sound was the ticking of the clock.

"Besides," continued the English captain. "You would be of great help to us. As you have guessed, I'm sure, we are planning to attack New Orleans. It would be to our advantage to be able to approach the city through your waterways. The twisting swamp lands are dangerous. But with your help, we could get through them safely."

The captain took a deep breath and stopped talking. He looked around at his two silent companions. Then he turned toward the pirate leader.

The pirate sat up straight. "Your plan seems almost perfect," he said.

The Englishmen smiled.

Then the pirate stood up. "My guests," he said. "I ask you

to excuse me for a short time. I must consult an old and wise friend. Then I shall return with my answer. Please make yourselves comfortable."

The pirate left the room. The three Englishmen sat quietly. Again they heard the ticking of the large clock. Then one of the officers walked over to the window and looked out.

He saw the pirate leader walk toward the mob still waiting on the beach. He watched him signal one of his men to join him.

"He is coming back to the house with one of his men," the officer said to the others. "What do you think?"

"I don't know," replied the captain. "He seemed interested. But I don't know."

The officer looked through the window again. He saw the band of pirates huddling together on the beach. They looked angry.

"The pirates are acting strangely," the officer said with alarm in his voice.

The two other officers rushed to the window.

The pirates seemed to be arguing. They were pointing toward the house and moving closer together. Now they were one large group. Slowly, the pirates began to march toward the house.

"They are coming for us," shouted one of the officers. "We must get away!"

"We can't get away," said the captain. "We are trapped here!"

The pirate mob was closer now. The Englishmen could hear them shouting.

"Spies!"

"Let's get the spies!"

"Death to the spies!"

The pirates reached the porch. They entered the front hall.

They burst into the dining room.

The Englishmen looked around. There was no escape.

"Get them—get them!" shouted the pirates. They surrounded the three officers. The Englishmen stiffened and stood close to one another.

They saw cutthroats, some bare-chested and some in silken shirts. They saw killers wearing pistols on each hip. They saw men with long scars across their faces. They saw pirates with wooden legs, with eye patches, and with long mustaches. They saw the terrible smugglers, the looters, and the murderers.

The Englishmen were silent in their fear.

"Grab them! Grab them!" shouted the pirates.

The Englishmen were forced from the dining room. They were pulled out from the house and down to the beach.

The pirates led them to a small building.

The mob pushed them into the open door. Then the door was slammed and locked.

The British officers began to yell, "Let us out!" They pounded on the door.

But the pirates just laughed.

Then the laughing stopped. There was no sound from the pirates.

They heard another sound—the voice of the pirate leader.

"Let them out!" he ordered.

The door was unlocked.

The pirate leader smiled at the Englishmen. He extended his hand to them. "Please accept my apologies for my men," he begged.

The Englishmen smiled weakly at him. They stepped out onto the beach.

"Gentlemen, forgive my men. They are an excitable group. Let me escort you to your boat."

"But what is your answer to our offer?" asked the captain.

"Captain, you see how my men feel. I will need time before I can give you an answer. Please return to your ship. Wait for two weeks. Then return to me, and I will give you my answer."

The three British officers entered their small boat. They rowed out into the bay to their waiting ship. Before long, the ship disappeared in the winding channels of the Louisiana coast.

Jean Laffite, the pirate leader in this story, already knew his answer. But he needed time. Within two weeks, he had notified the government of the United States that the British planned to attack New Orleans. Soon after, Jean Laffite held a meeting with the American general, Andrew Jackson.

Jean Laffite and his pirates joined the forces of General Jackson. Together they defeated the British at New Orleans. The President of the United States officially honored Laffite and his men for their contribution to the American victory in the War of 1812.

This story happened in 1814 on Barataria, an island in the Louisiana swamps.

After the war Jean Laffite returned to piracy. Finally, in 1821, his pirate colony was burned and Laffite sailed away, never to be heard from again.

Jean Laffite was both a criminal and a patriot. He was the last of the great pirates.

Some Other Books To Read

Pirate Lafitte and the Battle of New Orleans by Robert Tallant. Published by Random House, New York, 1951.

Pirates of the Spanish Main by the editors of American Heritage. Published by American Heritage Publishing Co., Inc., New York, 1961.

The Battle of New Orleans as seen and drawn by an American army engineer, and later engraved by the French painter and engraver, Debucourt. General Andrew Jackson is the one whose head is nearest the American Flag.

221

THE ROAD TO

Waterloo

By Jean Carper

We crouched low behind the ship's railing and held our muskets close to us. Through the gray haze of dawn came the call from a nearby ship, "Identify yourselves."

My heart jumped. Was our plan to fail now? On board our ship was the Emperor of France. I had been a soldier in his army for many years. I had been with him when his dreams for spreading his empire to all Europe had ended in defeat. I had grieved when he was taken from his throne and sent to the Island of Elba as a punishment. Now those of us who were still loyal to him had rescued him from his island prison and were taking him back to France to help him recapture his throne. Everything had gone smoothly until now. But why was this other ship stopping us? Had the Emperor's escape been discovered already?

We gave no answer. We could hear only
the sound of hushed voices and shuffling feet
on our deck.

"Be ready to fire," whispered our captain.

Again came the voice, "Ahoy! Ahoy there!
Who are you? Answer or we'll fire!"

Our captain stepped up behind me and
gripped the railing. He whispered nervously
to the man who squatted beside me, "What
shall I answer, sire? If they guess that you are
on board, they will sink us for sure."

"Answer him, but don't let him know I am
on board!" The words were stern. I quivered
with excitement. The man crouching close to
me was the Emperor himself!

Our captain shouted back, "We are the *In-
constant*. And who are you?"

"Oh, greetings, my good captain. We are
the *Zephyr*. We are patrolling these waters on
the lookout for the Emperor. There is a rumor
that he may try to escape from the Island of
Elba and return to France."

"I have heard no such rumor," replied our
captain.

"Why are you sailing so fast toward
France?" The tone was suspicious.

My finger tightened on the trigger of my
musket.

"We are merely going for supplies as we do
every month," our captain answered.

"All right. You are free to go. And happy
journey!"

We watched silently as the *Zephyr* faded
like a ghost into the morning mist. Then the
Emperor and I stood up.

The Emperor barely reached my chin. But
he looked strong and he had a powerful voice.

"Were you frightened?" he asked.

"A little, sire."

"No need to be afraid," he said.

I spoke boldly, "We shall soon land in France, and the French people will welcome you back to your throne."

"I hope so," replied the Emperor. "But I have many enemies in France. We will have to fight those who captured me and made me a prisoner on the Island of Elba. King Louis has many friends."

"You have many more, especially the soldiers," I replied.

"We shall soon know." He walked away with his hands clasped behind his back.

No one saw us land on the southern coast of France.

The Emperor sent a detail of soldiers to a nearby fort. "Find out if the commander is friendly. If he is, tell him that we have arrived."

We settled down on the beach. Hours passed and our soldiers did not return. It became dark and we made campfires from driftwood. Suddenly, we heard footsteps slushing through the sand. An old man with a wild look on his face stumbled into our camp.

"Emperor! Emperor!" he cried. "I heard you were here and came to warn you. The commander at the fort is loyal to the King. He has taken your soldiers prisoner and has sent messengers to warn the King that you are back in France."

"Then quick! We must travel with great speed!" ordered the Emperor. "We must start for Paris at once!"

On the first day of our march we passed through several towns. To our surprise, no one shot at us or cheered us. The people just stared curiously.

Then we trudged over snow-laden trails that wound around mountain peaks. My feet were numb. I was afraid I would slip and fall.

At last we reached the outskirts of a town. The Emperor signaled us to halt.

"Do you hear those church bells ringing in the distance?" he asked. "It is a bad sign. Someone has sighted us and now sounds the alarm. Be careful. The townspeople may shoot at us."

Cautiously, we marched into the town. Some people suddenly dashed toward us. I raised my musket. The Emperor drew back to give the signal to fire.

But the people shouted happily, "Long live the Emperor! Welcome back!"

The townspeople fell to their knees before him. They kissed the hem of his long coat. They kissed his sword. An old blind soldier begged to touch him. The Emperor, with a broad smile, patted the soldier on the back.

"But what were the bells we heard?" the Emperor asked.

"Why, only bells tolling for a funeral, sire," answered an old man.

We marched through the town, past the cheering people, and on toward Paris.

Just outside a nearby village we ran into trouble. A soldier from the front of our column ran breathlessly back to the Emperor. "The King's troops block our way."

"I will send an officer to talk with them. They must let us through," said the Emperor.

An officer ran toward the enemy lines. He returned shortly with bad news. "The commander says he is loyal to the King. He says he will take you prisoner or shoot you if you resist."

The Emperor's eyes blazed. "I once commanded those very same troops. We will see if they have nerve enough to shoot me."

Then he did a strange and bold thing. He stepped out from our ranks and walked alone toward the King's soldiers.

The commander saw him and yelled, "There he is! Fire!"

The soldiers seemed paralyzed. Not one pulled a trigger. The Emperor stepped closer. Still no one fired.

The Emperor opened wide his heavy overcoat. He slapped his chest and shouted, "Here I am! If there is any man among you who can kill me, shoot now!"

The soldiers trembled in awful silence. Then one of them ran toward the Emperor, shouting, "Down with the King! Long live the Emperor!"

Hundreds of others followed. With whoops of joy the soldiers ran to the Emperor and formed in ranks behind him.

All along the route to Paris, more soldiers joined us every day.

Citizens lined the streets to cheer us.

At last we were just outside Paris. We halted, waiting for the King's troops to attack us.

We expected the battle to begin any minute.

Then a messenger rode up to the Emperor and handed him a newspaper. Our Emperor read in a loud voice, "King Louis the Eighteenth and the Royal Family fled from Paris last night. They escaped under the cover of darkness when they heard the Emperor and his troops were nearing Paris. His Majesty the Emperor once more sits on the throne of France."

We all cheered loudly and threw our hats in the air.

We entered Paris in great celebration. Cannons roared a salute, and we sang as we marched. Some citizens wept quietly. Others crowded around the Emperor. When we reached the palace, the crowd lifted the Emperor onto their shoulders and carried him to the throne. He was once again the leader of France.

The Emperor of France in this story was Napoleon Bonaparte, a brilliant military leader. At one time his empire covered most of western and central Europe.

This story happened in March, 1815. Although Napoleon regained his throne, he did not keep it for very long. On June 18 of that same year he was defeated by the British at the Battle of Waterloo. This was one of the most important battles in history because it marked the end of Napoleon's power. Today, when someone is defeated or fails to achieve a goal, we say that he has met his Waterloo. Napoleon was captured and sent to the faraway island of St. Helena, where he died six years later.

Napoleon gave many things to the people of France. He made important changes in education and in government. His laws, which were called the Code of Napoleon, still exist in France today.

Some Other Books To Read

Napoleon and the Battle of Waterloo by Frances Winwar. Published by Random House, New York, 1953.

First Book of Kings by Douglas Newton. Published by Franklin Watts, Inc., New York, 1961.

Napoleon crossing the Alps, a painting by Jacques-Louis David.

"WE WILL DRIVE THEM INTO THE SEA!"

By Audrey J. Schuster

The general swung his leg over his horse and dropped to the ground. Wiping his forehead with his arm, he looked around him at the dusty camp. His soldiers were still straggling in. They looked thin and tired. Some soldiers were carrying others who were sick.

A colonel approached and saluted.

The general returned his salute. "We will rest here for awhile," the general said. "Then we will march against the Spaniards. We have waited long enough to drive them from our land."

"Of course, you are right," agreed the colonel. "But . . ." He hardly dared to look at the general. "But do you really think we can defeat them? I mean, there are so many of them and our men are tired from the long march and . . . ."

The general raised his hand. "That is enough!" he said sharply. Then his voice changed. "Do you realize what day this is?"

"Why, I think it is the fifth of July."

"Yes, the fifth of July," the general repeated, his eyes shining. "On this very day, eight years ago, we declared out independence from Spain. We had had enough suffering, enough cruelty. We said to the world, 'We have had enough of Spain. From now on we will rule ourselves.'" The general shrugged. "And here we are, still fighting to be free. Well, this time we will win that freedom!"

The colonel had been staring at his boots. Now he raised his head. "I am ashamed," he said. "With you to lead us, we cannot fail."

The general smiled. "Get some rest," he said. "Then we will take care of the Spaniards." He turned quickly and strode toward his tent.

As he raised the tent flap, he heard hoofbeats behind him. A horseman was galloping into camp. The general watched the man dismount and hurry toward him. It was his scout.

"General!" gasped the man.

The general patted him on the shoulder. "Come inside and catch your breath." The scout followed him into the tent and they sat down.

"Now, what is it?" asked the general.

The scout leaned forward and spoke almost in a whisper. "The people in the town told me. And then I rode out into the countryside to see for myself. General, the Spaniards have an army twice the size of ours. They know we are here, and they are on their way to attack us."

The general frowned. "Are you sure?"

"I saw them myself . . . a long line of them strung out over the countryside. They will be here in two or three days."

"We must keep this a secret until the men have regained their strength and we are ready," said the general. "Talk to no one. Do you understand?"

"Yes, sir," said the scout. He saluted and left.

For the next two days the general worked tirelessly to put new life into his army. He visited the people in the town and nearby villages, persuading more men to join him. He collected guns, ammunition, and food.

The general was pleased with his work, but on the third day he sensed that something was wrong. The men were very quiet as he walked among them. There seemed to be fewer men sitting around the fires.

The general called the colonel.

"Colonel, find the scout and have him brought to my tent immediately," the general ordered.

"Very good, my general," said the colonel with a salute.

The general was pacing back and forth when the colonel returned.

"Where is the scout?" the general demanded.

"He is nowhere to be found," the colonel replied. "One of the men told me that he saw him slip out of camp."

"What!"

"He is not the only one," added the colonel in a low voice.

The general slumped into a chair. "Go on," he said.

"My general, a number of soldiers have deserted, and others are talking about it. They say that the Spaniards have twice as many men as we do, and that they are about to attack us."

The general nodded slowly. "It is true . . . But we can beat them! I know it!"

He sprang out of his chair. "Call the men together," he ordered. "I want to talk to them."

When the men were lined up, the general strode out of his tent. He stopped before them. Then he began to walk slowly down the rows of men, his hands clasped behind him. His face looked like a storm that was about to break.

No one dared to move.

Suddenly he stepped back so that everyone could see him.

"Soldiers!" he shouted. "We have marched through rain and hail . . . through swamps and across the mountains. You have been hungry and cold. Many of your comrades have fallen along the way." He stopped for a moment and stared at them. "But you are the strong ones who have refused to turn back. Will you run now from the Spaniards?"

There was no sound from the soldiers standing at attention.

"Your countrymen are watching you. They look to you to save them from misery and slavery . . . Will you let them down?"

The soldiers lowered their eyes.

"No!" thundered the general, and every head snapped up.

"You have proved that you are strong and brave. You can defeat the Spaniards, because you are fighting to make your country free."

Thrilled by the words, the men began to cheer. The general raised his hand to quiet them.

"You have heard that an army of Spaniards is marching toward us . . . that they have twice as many men as we." He nodded his head. "That is true! But each man who has followed me is worth ten of them."

The soldiers threw back their shoulders and raised their heads higher as he continued.

"We soldiers of America will not sit like old women and wait for the Spaniards to pounce on us when they please. We will march out to meet them—now! And when we find them, we will drive them into the sea!"

The soldiers were all cheering now. Over the noise the general shouted, "To your horses!"

The men with horses ran to their animals and mounted quickly. The rest of the soldiers fell in line behind them. The general mounted his great white horse and rode to the head of the column.

"Now, soldiers, are you ready for battle?" he cried.

"Yes!" they roared, and their arms shot up in a salute.

"Then follow me . . . to victory!"

The General in this story was Simón Bolívar, one of the greatest generals in South American history.

The incident in this story took place in what is now Colombia, forty-three years after the United States had become a nation.

Inspired by General Bolívar's words, the army went on to victory and freed their country from Spanish rule. Five years later Bolívar helped to free all South America from the Spaniards. A new country was formed in South America and named Bolivia in his honor.

Simón Bolívar tried to unite all the countries of South America into one nation like the United States, but his plan failed.

Bolívar is remembered as one of the great heroes of South America. He is called "The Liberator," and "The George Washington of South America."

Some Other Books To Read

He Wouldn't Be King: The Story of Simón Bolívar by Nina Brown Baker. Published by Vanguard Press, New York, 1941.

Simón Bolívar by Nina B. Baker. Published by Webster Publishing Company, St. Louis, 1947.

Simón Bolívar, the Great Liberator by Arnold Whitridge. Published by Random House, New York, 1954.

Statue of Simón Bolívar, Lima, Peru

"We Need EIGHTEEN Tough Men"

By Barbara True

It was almost sunset.

Kit looked around the campfire at the faces of the forty trappers. Captain Ewing Young was speaking to them.

"We're going into Indian country," Captain Young said. "We'll need men who are tough. His voice was almost a husky whisper as he added, "We'll need men who can fight mountains as well as Indians!"

Captain Young rested his foot on a fallen tree trunk. "I can only take eighteen men with me!" he said. "The rest of you will take our furs back to Taos."

Only eighteen men! Kit's heart sank. He looked around at the trappers. They were real mountain men—all except him. He couldn't hope to be one of the eighteen. He was the youngest of all, and a tenderfoot besides.

Kit looked beyond the campfire to the grassy hill where the horses grazed peacefully. It seemed almost too peaceful, he thought. It seemed that a breathlessness had settled over the woods. He didn't like the woods as still as this. He looked at the trees that arched above them.

"What are you looking for, Kit?" one of the men asked, chuckling.

"It's pretty quiet in these woods," Kit answered. "There ought to be a birdcall or something at this time of day."

The trapper laughed. But Captain Young looked across the fire at Kit. "I was thinking the same thing myself," he said.

The trappers began talking as they waited for the captain to pick the men for the trip. They talked about the thickness of the beaver pelts. They discussed the trail back to Taos.

Kit couldn't stop thinking about the western country. The eighteen men who were to be selected would go into the Rocky Mountain territory. It had never been explored before. Just the thought of such a trip left Kit breathless. If only he could be one of the eighteen men chosen!

Captain Young began to call out the names of the men he wanted to take with him.

Kit kept count of the names as they were called. He counted ten, eleven, twelve.

The names came slower as Captain Young neared the end of the list.

Young called the fifteenth, then the sixteenth name. It seemed to Kit that the captain weighed the ability of each man in his mind as his eyes rested on each face.

He called the seventeenth name.

Lucky fellow, Kit thought to himself.

Captain Young looked around thoughtfully, searching each face for the eighteenth man. His eyes rested on Kit for a moment. Kit's heart leaped. But then the Captain looked past him to the next man.

Kit rested his elbows on his knees and gazed at the ground. Suddenly, a movement drew his attention toward the hill. The sun had dropped behind the grassy hill and had left the sky streaked with gold and pink. Kit saw the shadows of three Indians barely outlined against the sunset. They were creeping forward toward the horses.

"Captain, look!" Kit cried, pointing toward the hill.

Every man was on his feet in a second, rifle in hand. Now there were six Indians, then eight. They were still coming into view when Kit stopped counting them.

"There are dozens of them," Captain Young whispered.

He knew that the only chance the trappers had was to trick the Indians. He sent thirty of his men into the woods so the Indians would see only a small group.

"We'll let the Indians come into camp," Captain Young said. "If I raise my arm, fire hard and fast."

Kit ran toward the woods and dropped to the ground behind a large tree. He loaded his rifle and waited.

Captain Young stood in the middle of the packs of furs and camp equipment with ten of his boldest men. Kit watched from his hiding place as the Indians trailed into camp.

Their faces were covered with war paint of vivid red, blue, and yellow. Seeing only a small group of men, the Indians became bold and confident. They poked around among the furs. packs, and supplies.

242

The Captain made a sweeping gesture with his hand, motioning the Indians to leave. But they ignored him. He stepped in front of one of the braves. The brave shoved him aside roughly and sent him sprawling to the ground. The Captain picked himself up. He raised his arm.

That was the signal.

Instantly, rifles began firing. Indians yelled. Dust rose. Arrows and bullets filled the air. Wounded Indians staggered and made their way out of the camp site.

In spite of the confusion and the excitement, Kit kept firing his rifle. The Indians began to scurry up the hill, shooting arrows back at the camp as they went.

Just as the last few Indians were running from the camp, Kit saw a brave on top of the hill aiming his bow at Captain Young. As the Indian drew the bowstring back, Kit raced out of the woods and fired his rifle. The arrow whizzed from the Indian's bow but fell short of its target. Captain Young whirled around just in time to see the brave fall to the ground. The Captain looked at Kit and nodded his thanks.

To the Indians, it seemed as though shots were coming from everywhere as the men hidden in the woods kept up their steady fire. Soon there wasn't an Indian left in sight.

Captain Young signaled his men to return to the center of the camp. He laid down his rifle and looked around thoughtfully.

The plan had worked. Not one of the trappers had been hurt.

"Well, men, that was a close call," the Captain said. "If young Kit hadn't noticed those Indians when he did, some of us might not be here to tell the story."

Then Captain Young looked straight at Kit. "Looks like you've got the makings of a real mountain man. How about you coming West with us?"

Kit brushed a lock of hair from his forehead. "Sure, I want to come," he said.

Taos, New Mexico, as it looks today

The Kit in this story was Christopher (Kit) Carson for whom Carson City, Nevada, was named. Kit did many exciting and dangerous things in his life. He guided early settlers into the West. He rode the pony express. Later in his life Kit became an Indian agent in Taos, New Mexico, protecting white settlers from Indians and Indians from unjust white men.

This story took place in the 1820's. It happened before the Civil War and before the great gold rushes brought thousands of people to the West. That trip with Captain Young was the first of many trips into the wild West for Kit Carson. When he returned, he was a real mountain man able to lead other men across the Rockies.

Some Other Books To Read

Kit Carson, Mountain Man by Margaret E. Bell. Published by William Morrow and Co., Inc., New York, 1952.

Kit Carson and the Wild Frontier by Ralph Moody. Published by Random House, New York, 1955.

Kit Carson: Trail Blazer and Scout by Shannon Garst. Published by Julian Messner, Inc., New York, 1942.

TOM
AND THE THREE-FOOT PIKE

By Virginia Barrett Novinger

Tom Jackson trudged down the dusty road toward Jackson's Mill, Virginia, where he lived with his uncle. The dust sifted between his bare toes and felt warm and soft to his feet. Tom loved to go barefoot and didn't much like to think of winter when he would have to wear shoes.

Tom was eleven years old. It was a bright summer day, and he'd been fishing. Over his shoulder was a three-foot pike with the smooth end of a forked stick piercing its gills. Tom was small for his age, and at first glance it almost seemed that there was more fish than boy.

Tom shifted the weight of the fish to his other shoulder and walked on, kicking up the dust in little swirls. His old straw hat was low over his eyes to shade them from the hot sun.

It was a happy life at Jackson's Mill. Tom's uncle was a bachelor and had many hours after a day's work to spend with Tom and his brother. He taught the boys to hunt and to fish and to love outdoor sports.

Young Tom Jackson thought of this as he walked along the road, his fish over his shoulder, on the way to keep a bargain he had made with Conrad Kester, the village gunsmith. Tom was a great one to *make a bargain* and was very strict about *keeping a bargain.* He was known throughout the county for his honesty and his fairness.

And this bargain he'd made with Mr. Kester was for fish.

"I'll pay you fifty cents, Tom, for every fish you can bring me that is two feet long," Mr. Kester had said early that summer.

Tom had been pleased at the prospect of earning so much money.

"That's a bargain, Mr. Kester," Tom had replied, extending his right hand. "But that seems like a lot of money, just for fishing."

"Oh, that's all right," Mr. Kester had said, shaking hands to seal the bargain. "I can't leave my shop. And my wife and I do love a good fish dinner at least once a week. Why, you'll be doing us a favor, that you will."

"Well, if you say so, Mr. Kester," Tom had said. "I'll really do my best to bring you home some nice big pike."

"Pike! Now there's a fish for eatin', I'll be bound," said Mr. Kester, rubbing his fat stomach. "The wife 'll be glad to hear about this."

He had turned back into his gun shop, and soon the tink, tink, of his hammer on the anvil was heard.

Tom had fished many times that summer for Mr. Kester. Sometimes the fish hadn't measured quite two feet, and Tom worried that he wasn't keeping his part of the bargain.

Once Tom had mentioned this to Mr. Kester. Mr. Kester had said, "Now, Tom, that doesn't make any difference. Why, sakes alive, what's two inches when it comes to a fish as good-looking as this one."

"Well, Mr. Kester, you don't have to pay me the whole fifty cents if you don't want to," Tom had replied.

"Remember the fish last week that was two inches over two feet? You wouldn't take an extra nickel," Mr. Kester had answered.

"Yes, sir."

"Well now, this makes up for it," Mr. Kester had said with a big grin.

"All right, if you say so," Tom had finally conceded.

And now, as he scuffed along the road, Tom was really proud.

"I'll bet Mr. Kester will be surprised when he sees *this* fish!" he said aloud. When he realized that he had talked aloud he looked quickly around. It wouldn't do to be caught talking to himself. His brother, Warren, always laughed when he caught Tom talking to himself.

On the way to Jackson's Mill, Tom had to pass the plantation of wealthy old Colonel John Talbott. Colonel Talbott and Tom were good friends. And like everyone for miles around, the

Colonel was proud of the boy's honesty and good nature.

The Colonel was trimming a hedge along his driveway as Tom walked by, and he called, "Hey there, Tom Jackson, stop a minute and talk to an old friend."

"Oh yes, sir, Colonel. How are you this hot day?"

"Fair, son, just fair. This hedge been botherin' me, though. Couldn't see the road from my verandah, and, boy, I just can't sit there and not see the road. Might miss somethin'!"

Tom laughed, "You always have a joke, don't you, Colonel?"

"Been doin' any more fiddlin' at the hoedowns, Tom?" the Colonel asked, his blue eyes twinkling under snowy white eyebrows.

Tom blushed, "Now, Colonel, you're teasing me. You know I'm not a good fiddler. But I do like playing on my uncle's homemade fiddle."

"Well now, there isn't any call to blush, Tom," the Colonel said. "My goodness, the girls 'round here tell me you're a fine fiddler."

Tom blushed redder than ever at the mention of girls. "Aw, stop teasing me. I'm a better fisherman than I am a fiddler any day."

"Speakin' of fish," the Colonel said. "I'll give you a dollar for that fine pike you got there."

Tom laughed and shifted Old Pike around a bit. "Well, sir, I'm sorry, but I've already promised this fish to Conrad Kester."

"Hummmmph!" snorted the Colonel. "Bet he won't pay you a dollar for it."

"Nope, he's to give me fifty cents."

"Well, now, boy, I thought you were a better businessman than that," the Colonel said, reaching in his pocket for a dollar as if the matter were settled.

"But, sir, a bargain's a bargain. I promised Mr. Kester every fish I caught two feet long would be his for fifty cents."

The Colonel's eyebrows shot up. "But boy, this fish is all of a *yard* long! You goin' to let it go for fifty cents?"

"Yes, sir, I am. Mr. Kester has given me fifty cents for fish all summer, and some were not two feet long. This time he's goin' to get himself a real fish. For fifty cents!"

"Well, I declare," the Colonel said. "I do declare."

"But next time I catch a big one like this I'll ask Mr. Kester if it's all right for you to have it, Colonel. Will that be all right?"

"Sure, son, sure," the Colonel said. "My, you do stick to a bargain, don't you, boy?"

"Yes, sir, I try to, sir."

"Come see me again soon. I think you'd better get that fish in out of the sun!"

The Colonel winked at Tom and patted him on the shoulder. He gave him a friendly slap on the back and turned to his hedge.

Tom delivered the pike to Mr. Kester. Even the gunsmith was surprised at the size of the fish. "I'll give you a dollar for it, Tom. A bargain's a bargain, but this fish is worth a lot more than fifty cents."

"No, sir, Mr. Kester. I can't take any more than we agreed on. It wouldn't be right. Fifty cents is the price."

And fifty cents it was.

Young Tom Jackson left the gunsmith's shop, his fifty cents jingling in his pocket. He went back to his uncle's house and put the money into the cracked cup with the rest of his savings. The money was to go toward his education. Then, whistling a happy hoedown tune, Tom went outside to find his uncle.

This incident took place in 1835. Young Thomas Jonathan Jackson, who later became known as "Stonewall" Jackson, saved enough to complete his education at West Point. He served in the United States Army until the Civil War began. In defense of his own state of Virginia, he then became a general in the Confederate Army.

Stonewall Jackson was one of the greatest generals the United States has known. He was nicknamed "Stonewall" because of his ability to stand up against the enemy, no matter how fierce the battle.

All through his life as a soldier, Stonewall Jackson was known for his fairness, his loyalty to his men, and his strict honesty in the smallest details.

Some Other Books To Read

Young Stonewall, Tom Jackson by Helen Albee Monsell. Published by The Bobbs-Merrill Company, Inc., Indianapolis, 1953.

Stonewall Jackson by Jonathan Daniels. Published by Random House, New York, 1959.

Jackson Mills, boyhood home of Stonewall Jackson

The Alamo, San Antonio, Texas

The

By William O. Steele

Colonel's Last Fight

"Now I wonder how in thunder I can get Old Betsy out of the Alamo," the colonel said half-aloud.

He stood alone, leaning on his rifle and staring at the stockade fence that was built of logs and dirt.

"What's that you said, colonel?" asked a voice behind him.

The colonel wheeled to see who had overheard him. It was Micajah Autry, a friend of his from Tennessee. Autry was one of the twelve volunteers helping to defend this section of the Alamo's wall.

"If I was to tell you what I just said, you'd say that I ought to have my head examined," the colonel answered.

He took off his coonskin cap and scratched his head. "Or you might even reckon I ought to be hung up by my heels for the buzzards to eat."

"Oh, come, colonel," Autry said lightly. "No buzzard can eat anything hanging upside down."

There was a twinkle in the colonel's eye as he answered, "I reckon I'd go down a buzzard's throat mighty easy since folks say I am such a *slick* politician."

Autry laughed. "Colonel, you're the most cheerful man I have ever known. I've seen you cheering up the men with tall tales and with that old fiddle of yours. Why, I don't believe you've had a serious moment since we've been inside the Alamo."

The smile faded from the colonel's face. Dark lines of exhaustion took its place. He looked older than his fifty years. He knew that this was a very serious moment indeed for the men inside the Alamo. Few, if any, would escape with their lives.

But after a minute he spoke up cheerfully, "I believe in keeping up my spirits, no matter how black things look. But the truth is that I do have a serious problem right now."

"Maybe I can help you," Autry said. "What is it?"

"Well, I've been standing here trying to figure a way to get my rifle out of the fort before the Mexicans attack again," the colonel told him.

"You mean Old Betsy?" asked Autry.

"The very same."

He held up the rifle. It was a muzzle-loading flintlock, long and slim.

Autry was startled. "You—you aren't thinking of leaving the Alamo and taking Betsy with you, are you?"

"You know better than that," the colonel cried.

"I didn't mean any harm, colonel. I don't believe we could get along without you and Old Betsy."

"I never ran from a fight in my life, and I don't aim to start now," the colonel said. "My motto is, 'Be always sure you are right, then go ahead,' and I aim to go ahead and fight those Mexicans. It's the right thing to do, that's for sure."

Autry grinned.

"But I've been worrying about my family back in Tennessee since I found out that we have mighty little chance of leaving the Alamo alive," the colonel went on.

"I have been thinking about home myself," Autry said in a low voice. "I expect most men here have been thinking about their wives and children ever since they were given their choice of leaving the Alamo or staying here to die."

It was getting darker. The Mexican guns had stopped. There was a strange quiet in the Alamo. Behind the two men, fires were lighted to cook what little meat was left. Some of the men were collecting stones and piling them beside the cannons. These stones were all the ammunition they would have when the Mexicans attacked again.

"When a body hasn't long to live, he thinks of little things like promises and keepsakes," the colonel said. "My youngest son asked me for Old Betsy, and I promised him the rifle, straight out. A pa ought not to break a promise to his son. It's not right. I want that boy to have Old Betsy as a keepsake."

"It would be a shame to have Old Betsy fall into Mexican hands," Autry said.

"It would, for a fact," agreed the colonel. "But how in thunder am I going to get Betsy out of the Alamo and back to my boy in Tennessee?"

He glanced around.

"You reckon I could hide it somewhere with a note telling the finder what to do?" he asked.

"I know a better way than that," Autry said. "A messenger is leaving the fort as soon as it gets dark. Ask him to take Betsy."

"I'll be shot for a horse thief if you aren't the smartest one," the colonel said, slapping his friend on the back. "I'll do it right away."

He held up the rifle. "I'll kiss Old Betsy fare-thee-well, for she's the prettiest gal on either side of the Mississippi, and I'll be sorry to see her go."

The colonel started off across the courtyard. One of the soldiers at the cooking fires stopped him.

"Colonel, me and the men here would sure like to hear one last tune from you before we get to work repairing the walls."

The colonel grabbed the fiddle with a laugh. He gave the soldier his rifle. "Hold Old Betsy for me."

"I'd be mighty proud to do that," the soldier said, taking the weapon. He rubbed his hand along the barrel. "Knowing Old Betsy was here fighting for us has meant a lot to me and the others."

Several of the men behind him nodded in agreement.

"That's a mighty smart rifle, I'll tell you," the colonel said proudly. "She can sniff out a bear's trail good as any hound dog."

The men laughed.

"Can she play a fiddle sweet as you can, colonel?" asked a man.

"Oh, she can play as sweet but not as loud. Why, I'm the loudest fiddle player around. My wife wouldn't let me play my fiddle inside the cabin. She said it knocked the shingles loose. She made me go down into the hollow to practice."

The colonel looked at the faces of the men as they crowded around him. His heart was heavy. He didn't really feel like playing the fiddle and telling funny stories. But when he saw that they grinned and looked more cheerful as he talked, he knew he had to do it. For a few minutes he would help them to forget that they would never see their homes and families again.

"Once I took my fiddle and went down into the hollow to play," he went on. "I was a plumb fool not to take Old Betsy with me because as soon as I started to play, I was surrounded by a crowd of big old bears."

"How big?" yelled a man.

"Why, they were so big the sun couldn't get over them. It had to go around some other way."

The men roared with laughter.

"Those monstrous bears began to edge closer and closer. And I thought if I could knock shingles off a roof, I could knock down those bears if I played my fiddle real loud. So I played as loud as I could. It didn't stop them. They circled me, coming nearer with every step. So I began to play a real sad tune. Oh, it was so sad, those bears started crying. The sadder I played, the more they cried. Believe it or not, those bears cried so much they flooded that hollow with water and drowned themselves to death. And I floated safely away on my fiddle."

"Colonel, you're the biggest liar I ever heard!" exclaimed a man.

"Tell us another whopper!" begged the others.

But the colonel raised the fiddle to his chest and played a happy tune. He stamped one foot up and down in time to the music. When he stopped, the men called for another tune. But the colonel held up his hand.

"It's getting dark mighty fast," he told them. "And we have a heap to do to get ready for those Mexicans. We'd best get to work."

Smiling, the men drifted away to their jobs. The colonel picked up Old Betsy and headed toward the gates where the messenger waited for darkness so he could leave.

Now all I have to do is walk over and hand him my rifle, and he'll see to it that my boy in Tennessee gets Betsy, the colonel said to himself.

As he approached the rider, his steps grew slower and slower. At last he stopped.

Now didn't that fellow say that me and Old Betsy gave him confidence to fight, he asked himself. If Betsy is sent away, she'll be deserting right when we all need her most.

He turned away and thought, I won't do it!

Then he stopped and frowned, but I promised my son. And this rifle will give him something to remember me by.

Once more he headed for the gates. Thunderation, Old Betsy has got to get herself back to Tennessee.

The colonel hurried forward. In a moment the boy would be gone.

The colonel stopped and asked himself, but should I? This is likely to be my last fight, and I would like to have Betsy with me. He gritted his teeth, undecided about what to do. But confound it, he thought, a promise is a promise. I'm not going to break my promise to my boy.

"Ready for the gates to open, Jimmy?" the guard asked the rider.

The boy took a last look around the fort. He spied the colonel and rode toward him. "Just a minute," he called to the guards.

"Colonel," the messenger said.

"There is one thing I have been meaning to ask you. This will be my last chance."

"Fire away. Then I'll ask a favor of you."

"All right," the boy agreed. "That rifle of yours, Betsy, has it—has she really killed as many bears as folks say?"

The colonel nodded. "And more," he grinned. "Sometimes Old Betsy goes bear hunting without me. Hunts all by herself."

The boy laughed. "It sure has been a pleasure for me to know you and Old Betsy, sir," he said seriously. "Now, what was that favor you wanted?"

The colonel held the rifle toward the boy. Then he hesitated. Should he really part with Betsy? Wouldn't the others think he was giving up if he sent his famous rifle away?

"We're ready with the gate," called the guard.

"Just a minute," answered the messenger. "I have to go, colonel. What did you want, sir?"

Just then the colonel made up his mind. He knew that the right thing to do was to stay here and fight for freedom. And that was the right thing for Old Betsy, too.

He decided to keep Old Betsy with him. His son would understand.

"I—I just wanted you to tell Old Betsy good-by," the colonel told the messenger, lowering his rifle. "And to ask you as a favor to get safely through the Mexican lines."

"Thank you, colonel. Both of you." Jimmy leaned over and touched the rifle, then rode toward the gate.

In the darkness the colonel heard the bars of the gate slip to the ground. The horse moved outside. It was quiet beyond the walls. Suddenly, he heard the hoofs begin to beat the ground in a steady rhythm. The messenger was off!

The colonel went back to the stockade. He could see the dark figure of Micajah Autry standing guard by the cannon.

"Old Betsy wouldn't leave," the colonel said.

The colonel in this story was David Crockett, one of the most famous heroes in the history of the United States. Davy Crockett loved to tell tall tales about himself. These tales have become a part of American folklore. Many books have been written about the legend of Davy Crockett, but Davy was much more than a legend. He was a hunter, a scout, a soldier, and a congressman. He could have left the Alamo in San Antonio, Texas, before the last battle. But he fought because he believed in the principle of freedom.

When the Battle of the Alamo was over, Davy, like all the rest of the fighters, lay dead. Old Betsy was found beside him shattered past repair. But the courage of those soldiers back in 1836, helped lay the foundation of American freedom. They left us a valuable memory and that is why we say today—"Remember the Alamo!"

Some Other Books To Read

Chanticleer of Wilderness Road; a Story of Davy Crockett by Meridel Le Sueur. Published by Alfred A. Knopf, Inc., New York, 1951.

Davy Crockett's Earthquake by William O. Steele. Published by Harcourt, Brace and Co., Inc., New York, 1956.

Tall Tales of America by Irwin Shapiro. Published by Guild Press, Inc., New York, 1959.

Davy Crockett

Black Mike to the

Rescue

Jimmy sat alone almost hidden by the tall prairie grass. He had tried to be brave in front of Ma and Little Sister, but he was scared. And now that he was alone, he began to cry.

Jimmy and his family had been left behind by the wagon train when one of their horses had run off. By the time they had caught the horse, the other wagons were out of sight. They had followed the tracks to a river. But now their wagon was stuck in the sand of the riverbed. Pa had gone off yesterday to catch up with the wagon train and bring back help.

Pa had promised to be back before sundown yesterday. But he was almost a whole day late already. The family was nearly out of food, and Jimmy had set out to find a rabbit for supper. So far, he hadn't seen any kind of game at all.

What could have happened to Pa? Jimmy wondered. Maybe the Indians have ambushed and killed him! How could they get their wagon out of the sand? And what were they going to do about food?

If only we hadn't come out West, he said to himself. Then he remembered how excited he had been when his folks had decided to sell their farm and move to Oregon, after hearing a man make a speech about it.

Suddenly, Jimmy heard footsteps. He whirled around! Coming

By Enid Johnson

toward him was a strange-looking man with a black beard, wearing a buckskin suit with long fringes down the seams of his trousers. Strapped to his back was a pack made of buffalo skin that bulged with all sorts of things.

"Howdy, stranger," the man said in a kind voice. "Seems like you're in some kind of trouble."

"Y—Y—Yes, Sir," Jimmy replied, wiping his eyes.

"Tell me all about it, son," the man urged.

He seemed so friendly that Jimmy poured out the whole story.

When the stranger heard that Jimmy and his family had nothing to eat but potatoes, he said, "Let's go to your wagon. I've got some meat in my pack that I'll share with you folks, and when your Pa gets back, we'll see what we can do about getting your wagon out of the sand."

"Do you live around here, Mister?" Jimmy asked.

"Not anymore. I used to trap beaver hereabouts and sell their pelts to the fur companies. But the streams are pretty well cleaned out, so I'm going farther west to the mountains, where there's lots of beaver. Now let's go and cook the meat. By the time we've used it all up, I'll surely get a buffer."

Seeing Jimmy's puzzled look, he said, "So you don't know what a 'buffer' is. Well, that's what we trappers call buffalo."

"Are you a mountain man?" Jimmy asked.

"I sure am!" the stranger replied. "They call me 'Black Mike,' because of my black beard."

"My name's Jimmy," the boy said.

"Well, Jimmy, let's go back to that wagon of yours now and have some dinner."

When they reached the wagon, Jimmy noticed that Ma looked at the stranger as though she was scared of him. He *was* kind of rough looking, but Jimmy hoped that Ma would notice his kind blue eyes.

"Ma, this is Mr. Black Mike. Black Mike, this is my Ma."

"Pleased to meet you, Ma'am," Black Mike said. "I was just telling Jimmy that I've got some meat I'd like to share with you folks."

"Thank you, Black Mike. That's very kind of you," Ma said, holding out her hand.

Jimmy saw Black Mike wipe his palm on his jacket before tak-

ing Ma's hand. Black Mike seemed pleased that she wanted to shake hands with him.

Maybe he doesn't often get to talk to a lady like Ma, Jimmy thought.

Jimmy and Black Mike gathered firewood while Ma got the potatoes and coffee ready. When the fire was blazing, Black Mike took long, sharp, pointed sticks from his pack and put the meat on them. Little Sister came out of the door of the wagon when she smelled the meat cooking.

They sat around the fire to eat, and soon they had eaten every scrap.

After dinner, Black Mike stood looking at some things that other travelers had thrown away along the riverbank. "Golly, those people make themselves lots of trouble, with their heavy loads! They bring so much useless stuff along."

"We brought too much, ourselves, but we didn't know any better," Jimmy said. "The man who made a speech about how folks ought to go and settle in Oregon didn't say anything about that. He said lots of things that aren't true, though. Didn't he, Ma? And we believed him."

"He certainly painted a rosy picture of Oregon," Ma agreed.

"Oh, Oregon's a fine place," Black Mike told them. "It's getting there that's bad. What did the fellow say that isn't so, son?"

"Well, for one thing, he said we'd find lots of game along the way. He told us that the plains were 'black with buffalo'—those were his very words. And we haven't seen a buffalo yet! We were figuring on having lots of buffalo meat to eat."

"Just wait," Black Mike said. "You'll be seeing plenty from now on."

Next morning, Jimmy and Black Mike, carrying empty pails, went to get fresh water from a stream that emptied into the river.

"Let's take our rifles along, Jimmy," Black Mike said.

They hadn't gone three miles, when they heard a strange sound, like the bellowing of a big bull.

"Listen, son! Sounds like buffer!"

Soon they saw a procession of huge buffaloes, walking one behind the other, across a grassy hilltop.

"Let's get behind that big rock, Jimmy," Black Mike said. "When we get a chance we'll take a shot at one of them."

Soon they heard the thud-thud of the approaching buffaloes. A moment later, an enormous black head appeared above the long weeds and grass. Jimmy could just make out the animal's horns in its tangled mane of hair. Half-sliding, half-plunging, the great buffalo went into the river. Then it stepped out onto a sand bar, and bent its massive head down to drink. When it raised its head, the boy saw drops of water falling from its wet beard.

Black Mike cocked his rifle. Jimmy cocked his, too. Then the man rested his elbow on his knee, to make his aim steadier. The boy imitated him. Then, putting the stock of his gun against his shoulder, Black Mike sighted the buffalo along the barrel. Jimmy did the same.

Why doesn't he fire? Jimmy wondered. But Black Mike seemed in no hurry.

The buffalo, having drunk all it wanted, began to march slowly over the sands to the other side of the river.

"See that small bare spot just behind his

shoulder?" Black Mike whispered. "That's the place to aim for. Go ahead, son. He's all yours."

Jimmy pressed the trigger.

"Good boy!" Black Mike shouted. "You hit him!"

"Honest?" Jimmy asked. "He doesn't look hit, or even hurt!"

"Look at the bare spot now. See the red dot in the middle of it?"

Jimmy saw that the red dot was growing larger, but still nothing happened.

"Why doesn't he fall?" he asked.

"Wait a bit. He will."

Slowly the huge beast began to totter. Its knees bent under it. Its great head sank to the ground. Then its whole body swayed to one side, and it rolled over on the sand.

"Hurray!" cried Jimmy. "I got a buffalo! Let's go skin him!"

"Hold on, sonny," the trapper warned. "The rest of the herd are coming along. We'd be in a peck of trouble if we got mixed up with them."

271

A few seconds later, the whole herd came near the place where the dead buffalo lay. Paying no attention to it, each began to drink deeply from the stream.

After what seemed like hours to the boy, the herd of buffaloes turned around and galloped away. They had walked in one straight line, like marching soldiers, when they came to the stream to drink. Now they rushed pell-mell back across the prairie. Their pounding hoofs sounded like thunder.

As soon as the herd had gone, Jimmy and Black Mike began skinning the dead buffalo.

"Your folks are going to be mighty proud of you, son," Black Mike said. "You're a regular Daniel Boone. Now let's fetch some water and get back to the wagon."

They filled their pails and started for the wagon. But they were slowed down by their heavy loads of water and buffalo meat, and it took them some time.

Little Sister ran out to meet them. "Jimmy, Pa's back," she cried happily.

"Did he bring anyone back with him?" Jimmy asked.

"No, he couldn't find the wagon train. There were too many tracks going every which way," she answered. "But he's back and he's safe."

Soon they reached the wagon. Pa smiled at Jimmy and shook hands with Black Mike after Jimmy had introduced them.

"Ma and Little Sister told me about your sharing your meat with them last night," he said. "I'm mighty obliged to you, Black Mike."

"Well, now you'll have enough meat to last quite awhile," Black Mike said. "Jimmy here shot himself a big buffer. And he hit it right in the one spot that kills buffer sure."

Pa thumped Jimmy on the back. "Good boy," he said. "We've got a real hunter in the family. I'm proud of you, son."

Ma was too overcome to speak. But Little Sister jumped up and down and shouted, "Isn't my big brother wonderful?"

"He certainly is," Pa agreed. "At last we'll have some food to tide us over. But I guess we'll have to wait until another wagon train happens along and we can get our wagon out of the sand."

"That might take quite a spell," said Black Mike. "I'll show you how to get that wagon out. You'll be back on the trail in no time."

Young Jimmy, Ma, Pa, and Little Sister were members of a pioneer family going west along the Oregon Trail.

The pioneers would meet in Independence, Missouri. They would form wagon trains and follow the trail across prairies, plains, and mountains, almost all the way to the Pacific Ocean. A trip would take about six months. The pioneers faced many dangers along the trail. They often ran out of food, or were separated from their wagon trains. They faced terrible storms and Indian attacks. Some of the pioneers died along the trail. Others turned back.

Mountain men like Black Mike often came to their rescue, sometimes guiding the pioneers all the way to Oregon.

If you travel today along the land that was once the Oregon Trail, you can still see deep ruts made by wagon wheels.

Some Other Books To Read

Trails West and Men Who Made Them by Edith Dorian and W. N. Wilson. Published by McGraw-Hill Book Co., New York, 1955.

The First Book of the Oregon Trail by Walter Havighurst. Published by Franklin Watts, Inc., New York, 1960.

Oregon at Last! by A. Rutgers van der Loeff. Published by William Morrow and Co., Inc., New York, 1962.

Chimney Rock, Nebraska, a landmark of the old Oregon Trail as it looks today.

IN TERRIBLE DANGER

By T. Morris Longstreth

A tall, young U.S. Army captain and his scout silently climbed the mountain, over rocks, over fallen tree trunks, and through thickets. Slowly the two men climbed upward. Overhead, at the top of the mountain, they saw enemy cannons, but there were no signs of enemy soldiers. Only the occasional buzz of a mosquito broke the early morning stillness.

275

The United States Army was stalled in the middle of Mexico. In front of them was the mountain and the Mexican soldiers, with their cannons. On the right was a cliff, and the valley on the left seemed impassable.

The young captain and his scout were determined to find a break in the enemy's defenses because the army had to move ahead or admit defeat. So up they climbed, moving closer and closer to danger.

Suddenly the scout stopped dead in his tracks. He pointed down the slope. There was a path and beside it, only a few yards away, was a large spring. The path came from the south where the enemy camp lay.

They had found the way to the rear of the enemy fortress!

"I'll take a look up the path," the scout whispered. "It may lead to a road."

The scout started up the path. The captain leaned over the spring to take a cool drink of water. Then he pulled out his pad of paper and pencil and started to make a sketch of the area. He was so absorbed in what he was doing that the sound of voices startled him.

He stood tense, listening.

He heard Spanish being spoken, the language of the Mexicans. He saw no one. But the voices were coming closer.

What could the captain do? If he waited for the scout, he would be seen and shot. Then through the jungle of vines and leaves he caught a glimpse of an enemy soldier. The captain dropped flat on the ground. Ahead of him lay a huge log, half overgrown with bushes.

Swiftly he crept toward it. He crawled through the bushes and drew himself in close behind the log. His legs were very long, and he could not be sure that the bushes concealed every inch of him.

He hardly dared to breathe—the voices sounded so close. He heard husky laughs, shouts, and the sounds of men gulping as they swallowed the cold water. Their voices seemed right above him. How blind they were! Surely they should have noticed his boot prints. How lucky for him that these soldiers weren't American Indians! He would have been scalped by now.

The soldiers just seemed to stand around, talking and laughing. Would they never drink enough and go? How could the captain warn the scout?

But he soon became aware of other troubles. The spongy soil was wet after the winter rains. His clothing was absorbing the moisture like a sponge.

A mosquito buzzed in his ear. It landed on his neck, bit him, and left an itch to be remembered. The mosquito flew off, but it soon returned with the whole mosquito tribe. One settled on the captain's ear, others found his wrists and his legs. Why didn't the soldiers leave?

Soon the captain heard new voices coming down the path. He heard greetings, laughter, and then words that sounded harsh and angry.

Suddenly, two voices grew louder and shouts filled the air. An argument had flared up! Two of the soldiers were fighting, while the others egged them on. One of the fighters was knocked against the log.

The onlookers shouted. Again the victim was knocked against the log. Suppose he toppled over and landed behind the log? He would land right on the captain!

After what seemed like hours, the fight ended with a splash and a roar of laughter. The captain heard some of the soldiers walk away. But others came. The awful facts of the situation suddenly dawned on the captain. This spring must be the water supply for all the enemy soldiers camped on the slope. Nothing else could explain the coming and going of so many soldiers.

The captain knew that he might have to lie there all day. Ants had now come. They crawled under his shirt and bit him. They sneaked up his legs and bit. He could be eaten alive, but he didn't dare move.

Two voices sounded overhead! Were men peering down at him? Not yet. They must be sitting on the log with their backs to him. They smoked the most poisonous-smelling stuff. Some of it entered the captain's nostrils and he choked aloud. He was thankful that they didn't hear. He felt like sneezing. He pressed his head down into the soil and fought the tickle off. It was the closest call yet.

Now he noticed that a shaft of sunlight that shined through the leaves had moved as the day wore on. That sunlight could be his clock! He discovered that the light seemed to move faster when he lost himself in thought. He made an effort to take his mind off the danger—off the crawling ants and the buzzing mosquitoes, off the dampness of the ground and the agony of lying still. He tried to imagine what had become of his scout. Would the scout go back to the base? Would he return with a rescue squad?

Dreaming *did* speed the time. Now the captain felt cooler air along the ground. The shaft of light had nearly vanished, too. But soldiers still came noisily. Were they blind not to see that he was so near? Were there no dogs in the camp? What if some soldier brought his dog?

This new thought was so frightening that the captain forced it from his mind. The light was fading fast. Fewer soldiers were coming now. But the mosquitoes grew more numerous. The captain burned all over from his mosquito bites. But he was alive! What else mattered? He prayed that the scout had escaped.

Now the last soldier had gone. The captain waited, afraid to move. He was painfully stiff and thirsty. The sounds of water had tempted him for hours. Now he could drink. He listened. No human sound came.

He crawled slowly, noiselessly, to the spring. He drank and doused his aching face in the cool water. While he drank and doused again, he forgot to listen.

Suddenly, a dead twig nearby snapped like a firecracker. The captain started to rise, but he was too stiff to move quickly.

The approaching footsteps were almost upon him. He waited, holding his breath.

A voice called softly, "Captain, it's me!"

It was the scout!

"Here!" was all the captain could say.

"Thank heavens," the scout gripped his arm.

"Sshh!" the captain said. "Let's get away from here."

The name of the young captain in this story was Robert E. Lee, who later became the leader of the Southern forces during the Civil War.

Robert E. Lee managed to avoid capture by the enemy in this story and helped lead the United States Army to victory against Mexico because he was able to stay calm in a very dangerous situation. This same calmness helped him to win many victories all through his great career as a soldier. Though the South lost the Civil War, Lee's ability as a general was admired and respected by his own soldiers as well as by the soldiers of the North.

Lee is remembered as one of the greatest and most loved men in American history. If you visit Statuary Hall in Washington, D.C., you will see a statue of Robert E. Lee, representing his state of Virginia.

Some Other Books To Read

America's Robert E. Lee by Henry Steele Commager and Lynd Ward. Published by Houghton Mifflin Co., Boston, 1951.

The Story of Robert E. Lee by Iris Vinton. Published by Grosset and Dunlap, Inc., New York, 1952.

"Stop that Kid"

Will crept out of the house and into the barn where he saddled his horse, Prince. Then he leaped on the horse's back and went thundering out of the barn.

"Will! Stop!" his mother cried. "Where are you going?"

"To warn Dad," Will called back to her.

"You get yourself back in bed," his mother ordered. "You're sick with the shakes, boy!"

"Someone has got to warn Dad," Will shouted. "And there's no time to find anyone else."

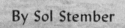
By Sol Stember

Will's mother knew how stubborn the boy could be. She also knew that someone had to go to warn her husband. So she reluctantly agreed to let Will go.

Before his mother could say another word, Will was gone.

As Prince galloped down the dirt road, Will thought about everything that had happened that morning. When he woke up, he had felt sick. His mother said he had a fever and had sent him back to bed. Hard as it was to stay in bed all day, Will knew that was the quickest way to get better.

But that was before he had heard the excited voices downstairs and found out that the Border Ruffians were planning to attack his father when he passed Stranger Creek. The Border Ruffians had vowed to get his father after the trouble he had with them earlier that year. Now his father was twenty-five miles away in a town called Grasshopper Falls and was coming home tomorrow. Someone had to get there quickly to warn him about the Border Ruffians.

So Will got dressed in a flash. When he was sure no one would see him, he sneaked down the stairs and out to the barn.

And here he was, sick with a fever, racing like a scared jack rabbit toward Grasshopper Falls.

Will felt better out in the fresh air riding along the dirt road. When the road turned south, Will left it and headed across open country. Stranger Creek was eight miles from his home. When he finally reached it, the sun was well on its way down the western sky. The breeze had died down. The air was hot and still.

Will rode up a rise of ground and stopped his pony. Down below was the creek. On the other side, the ground rose again in a steep hill. Beyond was the prairie stretching into the west for hundreds of miles.

Will looked around carefully. There was a clump of trees on his side of the creek a little way from the crossing place. Among the trees he could see horses grazing. The Border Ruffians were standing about or sitting on the ground resting against the trees. Will noticed that none of the horses had saddles on.

He started down the slope slowly, hoping the men below could not hear him coming. He hoped to get as close to the creek as he could before dashing across. Halfway down, Prince hit his hoof against a large stone. The stone started to roll. One of the men came to the edge of the trees and looked up. He saw Will and Prince.

Without waiting, Will loosed the reins and drove his heels into Prince's flanks.

"Come on, Prince! Let's show them how we can run! Whoo-ee!"

The pony whinnied and broke into a gallop. Prince thundered down the slope and headed right for the creek.

Some of the men ran out and tried to head Will off. But before they could stop him, Prince was down the bank and splashing through the shallow water.

Will heard a man shout, "Stop that kid before he gets to his Pa!"

Then Prince was scrambling up the other side and running up the hill. At the top, Will looked back. He saw the men below saddling their horses as fast as they could.

Will didn't wait to see any more. Ahead of him was nothing but open prairie. There was no place to hide. There was no friend in sight. There was nothing to do but run.

Prince put back his ears, stretched out his neck, and flew like the wind. Will prayed the brave pony would not step into a hole. If he did, that would be the end of the race. The Border Ruffians would catch them for sure.

Behind him he heard the thunder of chasing hoofs coming closer and closer. He looked over his shoulder. There was a rider just a few hundred yards behind.

"Faster, Prince! Faster!" begged the boy. "You've got to run faster!"

Prince ran faster than ever. Will looked back again. The man behind hadn't gained any, but neither had Will. It was a contest to see which horse would last longer.

Mile after mile of prairie grass flew by under the pounding hoofs. For a while, Will had forgotten about being sick. But now, he was beginning to feel hot and clammy. His stomach felt funny, and sometimes he saw spots before his eyes. He gripped the reins tighter and clenched his teeth. He knew he had to get to his father, no matter how he felt.

Suddenly, he remembered a farm where he had once stayed. It belonged to Mr. Hewette, a good friend of his father. Will knew that Mr. Hewette always had a couple of men around to help with the farm. If he could hold on until he reached the Hewette farm, he would be safe!

Prince galloped up a low rise of ground. On the horizon was a house with trees around it. It was the Hewette farm! They were going to make it!

Just then Prince stumbled! For an awful moment, Will thought the race was over, but the plucky pony recovered quickly and galloped on. Will looked back to see if the man behind had gained. He had! He was much closer! Prince was getting tired! His sides were heaving. His breath came in long gasps! His neck and flanks were covered with sweat.

Desperately, Will urged him on. A split rail fence flashed by. A small herd of cows scattered before him. The hoofs of the Ruffian's horse were coming closer and closer! Will could almost feel the hot breath of the Border Ruffian's horse on his back! He could hear the slap, slap of the reins as the man whipped his horse to go faster, faster!

But now the Hewette house and barn were just ahead. There was a man standing outside the barn door staring across the prairie at the racing horses. Will saw him turn his head. He must have called out because three men came out of the barn and joined him. They started to run forward.

Suddenly, there was a low rail fence in front of Prince. Will didn't see it in time to stop. He thought they would never make it. With all that was left in him, the gallant pony left the ground and sailed over the fence and into the Hewette barnyard. The Border Ruffian turned his horse and headed back. He knew he had lost.

Without getting down off Prince, Will told Mr. Hewette and his men the whole story. They were full of praise for his courage and daring, but when they tried to make him get off and rest, he refused.

"I've got to get on, Mr. Hewette," he protested. "I've got to get to Grasshopper Falls before Dad starts back."

Mr. Hewette chuckled.

"Will, I was over at the Falls just this morning. I saw your Dad and spoke with him, too. He told me he didn't expect to start for home before the end of the week. Besides, you can't ride any more today, son. You'll kill your horse if you ride him any farther."

Will tried to argue, but the barn and the trees and Mr. Hewette's broad, smiling face seemed to spin around him, and everything became blurred. Before he knew what was happening, Mr. Hewette had lifted him off Prince and was carrying him into the house.

The next thing he knew, he was tucked into bed, and Mrs. Hewette was feeding him a bowl of hot broth. It was delicious, but best of all, was the bed. It felt so good after his long ride that he became very sleepy.

Just before he closed his eyes, Will remembered something. He tried to sit up.

"What's wrong, Will?" asked Mr. Hewette holding him back gently with one hand.

"Prince—got to take care of Prince—" said Will drowsily.

"Don't you worry about him," replied the farmer. "One of my men walked him until he cooled down. Right now he has his nose in a pail of oats, and he is being rubbed down. Soon he'll be asleep, just like his master."

Will smiled gratefully, closed his eyes, and fell fast asleep.

In the morning Will woke up feeling much better. His fever was gone, and he seemed to be over the sickness. After breakfast, he thanked the Hewettes for all they had done and set off to ride the remaining five miles to Grasshopper Falls.

Later that morning, Will's father was amazed to see the boy ride up to him without warning. Will explained why he was there; and he told his father about his race with the Border Ruffians. His father listened without saying a word until Will had finished. Then, his eyes shining with pride, he put his arm around his son's shoulders and hugged him. Will thought that hug was the best part of the whole adventure.

The boy was Will Cody. He is best remembered for his skill as a buffalo hunter. In fact, he was so good at it, he was given a new name, a name by which he is remembered today—Buffalo Bill.

Will Cody grew up with the West. He drove long wagon trains across the plains. He was a pony express rider. Later he formed a wild West show, and took it all over the world to show people what life in the wild West had been like.

Buffalo Bill Cody was admired for his skill and bravery. But not many people knew that Buffalo Bill had had a lot of practice being brave. He had started when he was called Will and was only ten years old. In fact, not many people know it today. But you do!

Some Other Books To Read

Buffalo Bill, Boy of the Plains by Augusta Stevenson. Published by The Bobbs-Merrill Company, Inc., Indianapolis, 1948.

Buffalo Bill by Ingri M. and Edgar P. d'Aulaire. Published by Doubleday and Company, Inc., New York, 1952.

A SURPRISE ATTACK

By Clare Thorne

The crash of cannon and a volley of rifle fire woke the general with a start.

He rushed from his tent, shouting, "What is it?"

"Enemy soldiers, sir," one of his men answered. "There are hundreds of them firing from the mountainside just across the ravine."

"Take cover, men," the general ordered.

"What shall we do?" someone asked the general. "We don't have enough ammunition to keep firing back at them."

"We won't shoot back at all," said the general calmly. "We will ask them to surrender. Send a messenger with a flag of truce."

Surrender! It seemed almost laughable to expect such a thing. Why should hundreds of well-armed enemy soldiers surrender to just a few men?

But the general had given an order, and it must be obeyed.

A white cloth was tied to a stick and held high in the air. The enemy saw it and stopped firing. The messenger started to make his way along the trail, down the ravine and up the other side toward the enemy camp.

The general looked around at his small band of men. They had joined him in his march to free the city of Naples from the foreign king who held the city captive. They had camped on the side of this mountain for the night, planning to march on toward the city in the morning. This sudden attack by the enemy soldiers had taken them completely by surprise.

The general went back to his tent to await the messenger's return.

When the messenger returned, he found the general asleep. He woke him up to give his report. The enemy soldiers had refused to surrender!

"How many men do they have?" the general asked.

"At least a thousand."

"And they want to fight?"

"Yes, general."

"Very well, let them," said the general.

He rolled up again in his blanket and went back to sleep.

The men returned to their tasks. So long as the general showed no fear, they had courage enough to obey his commands.

Suddenly, a cannon ball landed right in the middle of the camp. It fell so close to the campfires that it scattered the cooking pots.

The general woke up a third time. "Go back to their lines and ask if they have decided to surrender yet," he ordered the messenger.

While the messenger made the trip down the ravine and up the other side, the general gathered his soldiers around him and began to repeat the lessons he had been teaching them ever since they began the march.

"Remember that we know the area better than our enemy does. We can attack suddenly and disappear before they recover from their surprise. We know secret paths which they do not know.

"We must always keep the enemy guessing about which is our main force. If we can make them follow a small part of our group, we can attack from the rear or from the side."

Soon the messenger returned from the enemy camp for the second time. His report was the same as before. "The enemy captain says that his soldiers want to fight."

"I have had enough of this captain!" shouted the general.

The rain of bullets had begun again. But the general waved his hand at them as if they were mosquitoes or flies. "Go back and tell the enemy captain that if he does not surrender in thirty minutes, we will attack!"

While this final message was being delivered, the general set about arranging his troops.

He quickly divided the fighting men into three small groups and one larger one. Each of the small groups was ordered to make its way in silence to a point near the enemy camp. One group was to go to the right, one to the left, and one behind.

"How many rifles do we have?" the general asked.

"Only five!"

"Good," said the general, as though five rifles were all he needed to attack a thousand enemy soldiers. "Keep two of them here with the larger group. Give one rifle to each of the three smaller groups.

"When you arrive at your points, wait for my signal," he told the three small groups.

"What will the signal be?"

"A trumpet blast."

Trumpets! They had not thought of that. With the general's soldiers were a dozen trumpeters who had volunteered to take part in the victory celebration on the day that Naples would be freed.

These trumpeters were divided as carefully as the rifles. Two went with each of the three scouting parties. The rest stayed with the general and the main force.

The general went on, "When the moment to attack comes, I will shout to each of my three groups in turn. Cannoneers! Sharpshooters! Lancers! And each of you will answer in turn— first with your trumpets, then with your gun!"

The boldness of the plan gave the men courage. The three tiny groups crept out into the darkness.

The general was calmer than ever. He said nothing, but every now and again he would take his gold watch out of his pocket.

"Twenty minutes have gone by," he said at last. "Our enemies have only ten more minutes to make up their minds."

Now for the first time the men began to think of what would happen at the end of those ten minutes. Brave and clever as the general's plan was, it seemed impossible for five rifles and twelve trumpets to defeat a thousand men.

"Six minutes to go," said the general. "Our groups must be in position by now. Are you all ready here?"

The men nodded and the two who had rifles got into position behind the rocks. The trumpeters raised their trumpets to their lips.

"Not yet!" the general warned. "There are still five more minutes."

They sat in silence waiting for the time to pass.

"Three minutes!"

Three minutes! The time dragged by. Would their daring plan work? Could a very few men defeat a thousand enemy soldiers by tricking them?

"Their time is up," said the general grimly. "Trumpeters ready! Sound the first call!"

The trumpets blared and the sound echoed back and forth across the mountainside.

There was absolute silence as the last echoes died away.

"Sharpshooters!" shouted the general.

Two trumpets answered him. They sounded like many as they echoed through the night. Then a shot rang out.

"Lancers!"

This time four trumpets blared. And now two rifles fired, one on each side of the enemy, the echoes making them sound like hundreds.

"Cannoneers!"

Again the trumpets blared and the rifles answered.

In the darkness and the clear mountain air, it sounded as if a whole army had encircled the enemy camp.

"Now," said the general. "Listen!"

There was silence.

Not a sound from anywhere.

Then at last a voice shouted from the enemy camp, "Surrender! We surrender!"

A dozen voices took up the call. Then hundreds! "We surrender!"

The battle was over. The general had won. His plan had worked.

The daring general in this story was Giuseppe Garibaldi, a military leader who fought to make Italy free.

This incident took place in southern Italy over one hundred years ago. After winning this battle General Garibaldi and his men marched on to Naples. The men he had captured joined forces with Garibaldi. Inside of a month, they conquered the city. Before many more years had passed, the city of Rome was conquered and became the capital of a united and free Italy.

General Garibaldi spent much of his life fighting to make Italy free. His courage and daring played an important part in uniting the kingdom of Italy.

Giuseppe Garibaldi

Some Other Books To Read

Garibaldi by Nina Brown Baker. Published by Vanguard Press, New York, 1944.

Garibaldi: Father of Modern Italy by Marcia Davenport. Published by Random House, New York, 1957.

WANTED:
young skinny wiry fellows

Fire!

A wall of flames spread across the horizon in front of the young rider and his pony.

The flames made the pony whinny with fear. Billy patted her neck, whispered, "Easy does it, girl," and jumped from the saddle. He held the pony's head against his shoulder and tickled her nose while he tried to think of a way to get through the fire.

By Robert West Howard

Billy knew he couldn't turn back. He dismissed the thought with an angry shake of his head. There were too many people depending on him. Across the desert other mail boys were waiting for their turn to carry the leather mail pouches. And it was up to Billy to carry the mail the first fifty miles from St. Joseph, Missouri, to the Seneca Station in Kansas.

Billy stared at the wall of flames and then at the dark clouds around the red sun. In those clouds could be rain and howling winds—perhaps even a tornado. A few hours from now a storm might put out the prairie fire. But Billy couldn't wait. He had to get through now! But how? He glanced from side to side trying to find an answer.

A half mile to his right, a line of bushes and cottonwood trees ran straight through the fire. Of course! He'd forgotten for the moment. There was a creek there! He could get through the flames by leading the pony through the creek. It might be a little warm, but they would be safe from the fire. Getting the leather mail pouches wet didn't matter. That storm would break loose with a lot more water before he could get to the Seneca Station.

It seemed strange that a fire so big should be roaring over the prairies this early in the spring! Someone may have left a campfire smoldering . . .

Then Billy remembered something. Back in St. Joseph when he started his ride, he had noticed a half-dozen Indians standing along the railroad station wall. Their black eyes took in everything. This could be an Indian trap. The fire could have been started by Indians to make him ride over to the creek. They might be waiting there to kill him. But that was the only way through the fire!

Billy slipped his revolver out of its holster, checked the bullets, and cocked the trigger. Then he tucked it back into the holster.

Even if there weren't any Indians, there was still the fire. His plan was to ride over to the bushes, blindfold the pony with his shirt, and lead her through the creek. As long as she didn't see the flames, she would be all right.

Billy mounted and turned the pony toward the line of bushes. The frightened pony reared and galloped off at full speed. Billy eased his body forward along her neck, the way Indians ride. His right hand lay against his gun, ready to whip it out at the first sign of trouble.

He reined to a stop as he reached the edge of the bushes. He remained perfectly still and listened. There was something moving in the bushes!

Billy's fingers closed around the gun. He walked the pony slowly through the bushes toward the creek.

Suddenly, a howling sound split the air and something crashed through the bushes behind him. Billy whipped out his gun and whirled around in the saddle.

It was a coyote! The pony must have frightened it!

Billy sighed with relief. He edged the pony down the bank of the creek and into the water.

He rode out to midstream. So far the water was only three feet deep. They should be able to make it without swimming. And there were no signs of Indians yet. He scrambled off the pony's back and into the water.

Dusk was rolling in. The shadows of the boulders and earth banks blended into the gray water. The smoke made his eyes smart and his throat tickle. Gun in hand, he led the pony up the creek toward the flames. The pony tugged back on the rein and whinnied. That did it! If there were any Indian ponies around, they would whinny back. He stood perfectly still.

Upstream something splashed and came leaping toward them. He held the gun ready to fire until he saw the shadow fill out to two deer and a fawn, running toward safety.

From the top of the bank he heard an owl hoot. After an

instant of silence another hoot came from behind them. Indians often signaled to one another with birdcalls and animal cries. Billy crouched against the pony's legs, studying the bank of flame just ahead for any tall shadows that could be Indians. The first owl hooted again. Then he could see its eyes, two bright twinkles reflecting the flames as the owl flapped up from a cottonwood tree and soared away to its mate.

Caressing the pony's trembling nose, Billy slipped off his shirt. He dropped it over the pony's head and tied the sleeves loosely beneath her jaws.

Funny thing about horses, Billy thought, they go berserk in a fire. But blindfolded and led by someone they trust, they will follow almost as gently as puppies.

The pony pranced and tugged back as she came close to the searing heat. "Easy," Billy whispered. "Another couple of minutes and we'll be safe."

They were surrounded by flames now. Both sides of the creek bank were ablaze. The smoke blinded him. He staggered straight ahead at a run, one arm out.

The words of that advertisement he had first read in the St. Joseph newspaper two months before raced through his mind.

WANTED
Young skinny wiry fellows not over eighteen. Must be expert riders willing to risk death daily. Orphans preferred. WAGES $25 per week. Apply, Central Overland Express.

Well, this was only the first 50 miles! Out there in the Rocky Mountains and the scorching desert the other fellows would have real trouble. They wouldn't get scared and choked up about some little thing like a prairie fire. They would have to face Indians and blizzards, deserts and grizzly bears, avalanches and floods.

Billy was almost through the flames now. He could see safety just ahead. But the smoke was filling his nostrils. He was getting dizzy. He seemed to be falling into a tunnel, down and down, with his lungs on fire.

Billy woke and found himself sprawled on the creek bank, the cool water sloshing across his shoulders, the pony nuzzling his neck. The flames crackled several yards behind them. The air was sweet and clean. He sucked it in, stood up, and shook himself. There had been no Indians.

He had made it!

The pony had worked the shirt most of the way off, nudging him. Billy tossed it back across the saddle and led her up the bank.

The western sky spit lightning. The thunder muttered like a hundred bulls bellowing a long way off. His hands felt carefully down the leather blanket and across each mail pouch. Everything seemed to be in good shape.

"Let's go," he whispered and squished back into the saddle. "We're going to be about an hour late, I reckon."

Billy Richardson, the young man in the story, was one of the first pony express riders. His ride took place in April, 1860.

For the next year and a half, the pony express riders carried the mail from St. Joseph, Missouri, to San Francisco, California. The last pony express ride was made in October, 1861. After that, the pony express was not needed because telegraph wires had been stretched across the "great desert."

On his first ride, Billy Richardson arrived at the station in Seneca, Kansas, an hour and a half late, slowed by the storm. Billy passed the mailbags along to Jim Beatley, who raced west on his fifty-mile run. The mail arrived in San Francisco ten days later.

Some Other Books To Read

The Pony Express by Samuel Hopkins Adams. Published by Random House, New York, 1950.

Riders of the Pony Express by Ralph Moody. Published by Houghton Mifflin Co., Boston, 1958.

"WE ARE GOING TO

One night during the Civil War, twenty-one Northern soldiers, wearing civilian clothes, gathered in a forest clearing. A tall, bearded man looked around at the group and said, "Glad to see you could make it, gentlemen. Before I tell you about our plans, I must warn you that there are extreme dangers involved. If you are caught, you will be hanged as spies. Anyone who wants to leave may do so now. Nothing will be held against you if you do. But once I tell you the plans, you will have to stay."

Not a man moved. Nor did anyone speak.

"Good! You are brave soldiers," the bearded man told them. "This morning, we are going to steal a northbound Rebel train right from under the noses of the Rebels!"

The soldiers looked at each other in surprise.

"We will run it north until we meet General Mitchel's troops who will be pushing down into southern territory. But we will do more than just steal a Rebel train! We are going to tear up track and burn railroad bridges behind us as we go. We will cut telegraph wires and destroy communications along one hundred and thirty miles of railroad track. If we succeed, we will destroy any Southern defense against General Mitchel's troops. And we will shorten this war by months!"

The buzz of excitement that followed was broken by Sergeant-Major Ross. "But, sir, how are we going to steal that train with all those Rebels around?"

"We will all buy tickets on the train. After boarding the train,

"STEAL A TRAIN!"

By Ann R. Leo

we will take seats in the same car. We will ride as passengers as far as the first stop, Big Shanty. When the train stops at Big Shanty, stay in your seats until I tell you to go.

"Will Knight, you will be the engineer. Be ready to follow me out of the passenger car. When I give you a signal, I want you to uncouple the locomotive and a few boxcars from the rest of the train. Then scoot for the locomotive cab! Be ready for a quick getaway!"

The raiders felt their bodies tighten with excitement. The bearded man continued, telling each man what his job would be when the plan would be put into effect.

When he had finished, the bearded man looked at Sergeant-Major Ross and said, "As top-ranking soldier, you are in command of the men who will ride in the boxcars. See that they get aboard the cars smoothly and quickly. We will have only about fifteen seconds to get aboard and get moving."

Ross hesitated a moment. Then he said, "But there are four Rebel regiments camped next to the tracks at Big Shanty! If they see us stealing that train, the whole camp will come swarming down on us!"

"That's right," the bearded man answered. "The success of the raid depends on how fast you can move your men without attracting attention. And if you do stir those Rebels up, shoot—and shoot straight!"

Then the bearded man lowered his voice, "Boys, I think we

307

will make it. I will succeed or die in Dixie!"

None of the soldiers said a word. Some checked their pistols. Others shook hands with the bearded man. They slipped quietly out of the forest, one by one.

"Big Shanty! Twenty minutes stop for breakfast!" called the train conductor as he walked through the coaches. Sleepy passengers stumbled toward the door. Twenty-two pairs of eyes watched them leave.

The tall, bearded man awoke from a nap. He got up, stretched, and started down the aisle. Tapping his tall silk hat firmly on his head, he casually touched the arm of Will Knight. Knight got up and followed him.

A tired Southern sentry paced back and forth alongside the train. Hundreds of Southern tents were pitched a short distance from the tracks. Will Knight followed the bearded man past the sentry toward the locomotive. The two figures strolled forward and peered into the locomotive cab. It was empty.

"So far, so good," said the bearded man. "Let's go back now and uncouple the boxcars."

Casually, they walked back past the three boxcars behind the engine.

So far, the Rebel troops had paid no attention to them.

Without turning his head, the bearded man whispered, "Uncouple here! Then try to get back to the locomotive cab without being seen. Hurry!"

The bearded man walked briskly back to the passenger coach. Inside he gave a quick smile, "Come on, boys, it's time to go."

The Northern soldiers headed for the door.

This was the crucial moment. If they were noticed now, the whole plan could fail. They raced alongside the tracks in full view of the Southern camp.

Three of the Northern soldiers climbed into the cab. Will Knight was already there with his hand on the throttle. The bearded man watched the last of the raiders tumble into the boxcars. Then he leaped into the cab.

"Let 'er rip, Knight!" he sang out.

The engineer pulled the throttle halfway open. The wheels spun on the track!

But the train did not move!

In his rush to get away, Knight had opened the throttle too wide. The wheels were spinning too quickly to grab on the slippery rails.

The sound of the spinning wheels made the sleepy sentry jerk his head. He stared at the throbbing engine. He was too surprised to move!

At any minute the whole Rebel camp would be alerted!

Will Knight swung the throttle trying to slow the spinning wheels.

Chug! The wheels grabbed! The train leaped forward, hurling the raiders to the floor.

Chug-chug! The locomotive began to grind along the track, building up speed.

The amazed southern sentry just stood and gaped at the train. Chug-chug-chug-chug!

By now the Southern troops saw what was happening. Officers were barking out orders. Soldiers were jumping to their feet.

But it was too late! The train was racing along at full speed—racing north to meet General Mitchel.

"Yowie!" yelled Sergeant-Major Ross in the cab. "We made it! We made it!"

The bearded man grinned at the cheering raiders. He murmured with satisfaction, "General Mitchel—here we come!"

The bearded man who stole the train was James J. Andrews, a spy for the Northern army during the American Civil War. General Mitchel's plan was to capture the city of Chattanooga, Tennessee, from the Southern forces. J. J. Andrews and his raiders were to destroy the railroad tracks and the communications south of Chattanooga while Mitchel would march in from the north.

Andrews and his men tore up track behind them. They cut telegraph lines. But they were followed by a Southern conductor, William A. Fuller, in one of the most thrilling chases in history. Nothing Andrews could do would stop Fuller. Finally, the stolen train ran out of fuel, and J. J. Andrews and his men were captured.

General Mitchel did not capture Chattanooga. But thanks to J. J. Andrews and his daring raiders, Mitchel was able to defend an important part of the railroad long enough to give the Northern forces an advantage in that part of the country.

J. J. Andrews and seven of his men were hanged as spies. The other raiders returned to the north to tell the story of the chase.

Some Other Books To Read

Stolen Train by Robert Ashley. Published by The John C. Winston Co., Philadelphia, 1953.

The Andrews Raid: The Great Locomotive Chase by Beryl and Samuel Epstein. Published by Coward-McCann, Inc., New York, 1956.

BELLE BOYD,
LADY SPY

By Marjorie L. Knight

It was a spring day during the early part of the war between the Northern states and the Southern states. A teen-aged girl named Belle Boyd sat in the living room of her aunt's home in Front Royal, Virginia. She was reading to her aunt and a friend as they sewed.

But Belle's mind was not on what she was reading. She was thinking about the rumor that General Stonewall Jackson and his Confederate soldiers were heading toward Front Royal. Belle hoped they would drive the Northern soldiers out of the city. While she read, Belle was thinking about the plans she had made to help General Jackson. If General Jackson came, she was to get word to him about his chances of capturing the town.

Suddenly, Belle's thoughts were interrupted. Her maid, Liza, ran into the living room shouting, "Miss Belle! Miss Belle! General Jackson is coming!"

Belle was on her feet instantly. Her book dropped unnoticed to the floor. "Liza! Are you sure?" she cried.

Too breathless to say more, the maid nodded.

Without a word Belle flung the door open and rushed out into the street. There was no time to lose! She had to learn the Northern soldiers' plans and get the information to General Jackson immediately.

There was confusion everywhere. Fleeing Northern soldiers scurried about without seeming to know where they were going. Horses pulled half-loaded wagons past Belle.

Belle seized a soldier by the arm. "What's happening?" she demanded. "Where is everyone going?"

Roughly brushing her aside, the soldier answered, "Ma'am, I'm a busy man. There's work to be done. Go home and stay out of the way. This is no place for a woman!"

Suddenly, Belle spotted an officer talking to one of his men. If only she could get close enough to hear them, perhaps she could find out what the Northern troops were planning to do!

Belle moved down the street. When she was within earshot of the officer and his soldier, she stopped. The officer turned to look at her. Belle pretended to be searching for someone among the soldiers who were leading the wagons out of town. The officer turned back to the soldier.

"Move as many of the supplies as possible out of town," she heard him say. "Burn the rest. We don't want to leave anything behind for the Confederates. My men will join General Banks on the other side of town. I'm counting on you to hold the town and stall the Confederates until we can reach General Banks. Then retreat and burn the bridges after you cross them. That way we can trap the Confederates here without food and force them to surrender when we ride back with General Banks' troops."

Belle turned and walked down to the end of the street. She

walked slowly so the soldiers wouldn't know she had overheard them. As soon as she was out of the soldiers' sight, she began to run. She rushed up the stairs of her aunt's house to the second floor, picked up a pair of field glasses, and hurried out onto the balcony.

Belle could see the advance guard of General Jackson's army three-quarters of a mile away marching toward the town. There wasn't a minute to lose.

Belle knew she had to get her information to General Jackson at once. If the general continued his advance on the town, he would surely take it. But if General Jackson did not follow the fleeing Northern soldiers, they would have time to join General Banks. The scattered Northern forces in the area would then have time to unite. And if they did, General Jackson would be trapped at Front Royal!

Belle grabbed the white bonnet she was supposed to use to signal the Southern troops. She ran downstairs, out of the house, and into the town. Without taking further time to think, she rushed back down the street. It was still filled with Northern soldiers and wagons. Everything was in such confusion that no one paid any attention to Belle. Soon she was out of town, running across the open fields—fields that might at any moment turn into battlefields.

On she ran, paying no attention to either weeds or fences. She scrambled up a ravine, waving the white bonnet at the approaching Confederates as she tried desperately to signal them.

Suddenly, realizing that her signals could also be seen by the Northern troops camped outside town, Belle tried to keep behind cover. But hiding was impossible. The Northern troops quickly sighted her and began firing.

Bullets fell all around her, some only a few yards away. Tired now and on rougher ground, Belle fell again and again. Each time she picked herself up and went onward. When she drew closer to the Confederate advance guard, she waved them on with the white bonnet.

The two units of the advance guard saw her bonnet. Without waiting for any further orders, they sped past her and dashed on toward the town.

Then Belle had a moment of great fear. The main body of the Confederate army was still hidden from her sight beyond a small hill. If the army were not so large as she had thought, it would mean that she had just waved her own men on to certain death.

Belle said a short prayer and pressed on. To her great relief, she caught sight of the Confederate main body. Yes! There were enough men.

Taking only enough time to catch her breath, Belle gasped out the information that the cavalry should hurry on to seize the bridges before the Northerners could destroy them.

The information Belle gave to General Jackson that day enabled him to win the battle of Front Royal. She continued to give information to the Confederate armies and fought as bravely for the South as any soldier. Several times Belle was captured, sent to prison, and then released. The third time she was put in prison she was placed under the care of a young Northern officer, Sam Wylde Hardinge. The young man admired Belle's courage and beauty. When she was released, he took her to England where they were married. After the war was over, Belle wrote the story of her many adventures in the book called, *Belle Boyd in Camp and Prison.*

Some Other Books To Read

In Calico and Crinoline; True Stories of American Women by Eleanor Sickels. Published by The Viking Press, New York, 1935.

The Civil War by Fletcher Pratt. Published by Doubleday and Company, Inc., New York, 1955.

LONG NIGHT ON THE CHISHOLM

By Beth Margo

Beside a sandy creek in northern Texas, an excited pinto pony jumped nervously as Jim tried to comfort it.

"Easy, girl!" he said as he caught the bridle. "We can't have you running off in the night."

The pony stood shivering as Jim rubbed the front of its nose. Looking up, Jim saw the trail boss riding over to him.

"Having trouble?" the trail boss asked.

"No trouble. They're a mite jumpy, that's all."

"That's another bad sign," said the trail boss frowning.

"Sign of what?" said Jim.

"Indians. Horses can tell when Indians are around."

Jim looked at the close-packed horses. Most of them were tossing their manes and stamping and skittering about.

"Could be they smell a mountain lion."

"Wish you were right," said the trail boss. "But we've been seeing signs of Indians all day. Maybe they've passed by, but from the way the ponies are acting I don't know."

Indians! Jim thought. If they steal our horses, then what will we do? We'll be a hundred miles from nowhere with no water except for a few creeks miles apart. If we get stranded here without horses, we'll never make it to Abilene, Kansas.

"You take the first watch with the horses tonight, Jim," the trail boss said.

"Okay," said Jim. He hoped that the boss wouldn't see that he was afraid. Only a tenderfoot showed that he was afraid, and Jim wanted the crew to forget that this was his first trip on the Chisholm Trail.

The trail boss helped Jim herd the horses into a nearby clearing that was surrounded by cedar trees.

TRAIL

"Keep a sharp lookout, lad," the trail boss warned and rode off.

Jim cocked his rifle and cradled it in his arms. He turned his head slowly, peering at the woods and rocks. The weight of the rifle was comforting. He wouldn't let it out of his hands till the next man came to relieve him.

The horses were neighing and shuffling, milling about as if they had stepped on an anthill.

"Whoa, there!" Jim cried and galloped off to herd a pony out of the brush. He circled the edge of the clearing, shoving the horses back toward the center, humming under his breath. Here we are, he thought, twelve men to keep sixty horses and thousands of head of cattle from running off into the desert. And now we have to run into signs of Indians.

Here in the shadow of the cedars it was already dark. Jim shivered as he watched the men rolling up in their blankets around the campfire. He wished he'd brought his blanket. It turned cold on the desert when the sun went down.

Reining his horse, he turned back to circle the herd. The cedars seemed like a black wall all around. Anyone could be lurking among those trees and you'd never know it. Not till they came out or shot at you. Jim wondered why the trail boss didn't put an extra man on this watch.

His horse whinnied as if in pain. Jim wheeled quickly, but he

saw nothing. He sniffed the air. I can't smell a thing, he thought. But the horses can.

No use thinking like that, he told himself sharply. You've got a job to do, and it's a tough one.

He slowed his horse to a trot, driving himself between the herd of horses and the trees. Got to keep them crammed together as tight as I can, he thought, dodging the cedar branches that whipped across his face.

Time dragged by and the night deepened. His shirt, wet from hard riding, slapped against his shoulders like a cold mop. Jim felt as though he'd already stood watch the whole night through.

Finally, when he was beginning to think he had been forgotten, he saw a rider jogging toward the woods. Jim rode out to meet him. It was Frank, one of the old-timers. Frank had his bed blanket wrapped over his head and shoulders, Indian style, to protect him from the chill.

"You'll have to ride hard to hold them tonight," he told Frank as they passed each other.

"Whew! Those woods are blacker than the inside of a buffalo," said Frank. "Anything stirring out there?"

"Nothing you can see," said Jim. "Good luck!"

The campfire had burned down to embers, and the sleeping men were sprawled around it. Thankful for the warmth, Jim swung down from his horse.

Crack!

Shots rang out from the woods behind him. They came from the spot he had just left.

His horse whimpered, toppled, and fell dead as the bullet struck. Whirling, Jim fired in the direction of the rifle flashes. He flung himself flat on the ground. All around Jim, men were diving for cover. Jim crawled away from the fire and wriggled under the low branches of a cedar tree.

The earth beneath him vibrated with hoofs, and he saw the horses pounding toward the camp. He remembered that earlier that day he had strung a rope fence between the wagon wheels and the trees, in case of trouble. Would the rope fence hold?

Now the horses were tearing through camp, leaping over the fire, crashing against the wagon. Some tripped on the ropes, others ran into them. And then the rush of the stampeding horses turned the wagon over. Jim heard a wheel splinter.

Off near the woods, there were Indian war whoops.

Neighing frantically, the few horses that were tied in camp reared and struggled to break their ropes. Some broke free and

galloped off after the rest of the herd. On the far side of camp, Jim could see the horses bearing down on the cattle like an avalanche. And then the cattle started to run. This was a stampede, something that every cowboy dreaded.

A horse tied to a branch reared above Jim, fighting to break its rope. Jim lay frozen with his arms over his head and thought, I'm alive! I'm alive! The Indians can't get me here. If I lie right here, who will miss me in all this yelling and crashing confusion?

But he knew what Frank would say to that, "A tenderfoot from Michigan. And a coward, too."

But it's stupid to go out, he argued with himself. Those Indians not only have arrows, they have guns, too. And they can see in the dark as well as mountain lions. I can't see a thing.

If they run off with our cattle, we lose the whole year's work, he thought. Still, isn't it better to be alive?

But where is Frank? Maybe he's wounded out there in the bushes. Maybe the Indians have carried him off.

Suddenly, Jim jumped to his feet. He seized the rope that was tied to the horse by the tree and leaped onto the horse's back.

With a quick slice of his knife, he cut the rope and clung tightly as the horse plunged toward the stampeding herd. He fought the horse, jerking and hauling on the rope until he managed to turn and head for the clearing where he had last seen Frank.

"Shoot, Frank! Shoot so I can see where you are!" he yelled. But there were no gun flashes.

If only he had some kind of light. Branches whacked across his chest as he rode around the edge of the clearing. How could he spot Frank in this blackness? Would some Indian arrow find him before he could get to Frank?

"Jim, is that you?" called a voice to his right.

Jim galloped over. When he was almost on him, he saw Frank propped against a rock.

Jim bent over him. "Are you hit bad?"

"Just winged me. It's nothing. Give me a hand, boy."

Jim helped him up. "Where's your horse?"

"He was shot. The Indians took the rest of the horses. They must have sneaked in and cut them loose."

"Climb up behind me and I'll get you back to camp," Jim shouted.

"Tarnation, lad, we don't want camp!" Holding Jim's arm with his good hand, Frank pulled himself painfully onto the horse's back.

"Cut around those far woods, then to the right—I think I know where they took the horses," Frank told him.

"But your arm. It's bleeding. Shouldn't we—"

"Do as I say," Frank said, slapping the pony's side.

The animal lurched forward around the cedars. "I know this country. If they kept on the way they were heading, there's just a chance—"

"But you're in no fit shape," yelled Jim.

"I'm in no fit shape to get stranded here without a horse," Frank said sharply. "Turn here, lad, and ride toward that gulch."

Jim could see nothing. But he could hear the other men yelling from far away to the left.

"There's a canyon there by the creek," Frank said. "It's just beyond those rocks. Listen!"

Jim reined up. With his free hand he held his rifle ready. He could hear horses neighing and Indians shouting.

"If they accidentally got the horses penned in there—" Jim said.

"Maybe they can't get them backed out," finished Frank. "Let's go."

As they raced toward the mouth of the canyon, an arrow whizzed past Jim's head. He swerved, lying low over the pony's back. He heard a shot and saw the rifle flash. Gripping the horse with his knees, he fired at the flash. Dimly he caught sight of shadowy riders galloping off, and he fired again. Answering shots from cowboys somewhere beyond the fleeing Indians showed that his gunfire had alerted the rest of the crew.

Frank's gun went off close to his ear, and he heard Frank moan, "No good with my left hand—"

"Never mind, just hang on. I've got the range," yelled Jim.

He kept shooting blindly toward the racing shadows. The pounding hoofs died out, and he could hear nothing but the frantic neighing of the horses. They sounded quite near! He rounded a pile of stones, heading in the direction of the sound. Just ahead of him he could make out the ponies rearing and pawing at the stony edges of the canyon where they were trapped.

Jim jumped off his horse and onto a fresh one. He helped Frank mount another horse.

"Let's go, Jim!" Frank shouted. "We've got hard riding ahead of us to get these ponies out of here and back to camp."

Jim and Frank circled the herd, collected the strays, and headed them back toward camp. Most of the horses had been saved!

As they rode back, Jim could see the dark mass of the cattle herd some distance away.

"I guess the boys are all right," Frank said. "They must have stopped the cattle stampede. And thanks to you we caught the horses. You'll make a first-rate hand, Jim."

"Thanks, Frank," Jim answered. He remembered how afraid he had felt lying under the tree. But Frank didn't know about that. And it didn't matter now. They had caught the ponies.

It had been a hard night's work, but suddenly Jim knew he wouldn't trade his job on the Chisholm Trail for a thousand peaceful nights in a farmhouse feather bed.

Many cowboys, such as Jim, took part in the long cattle drives from Texas to Kansas. They played an important role in the early history of the West.

This story took place along the Chisholm Trail. In the years just after the Civil War, the cattlemen used the Chisholm Trail to move herds from the Texas cattle lands to the railroads in Kansas. Many cowboys rode along the trail, and many died there. And like Jim, most of the cowboys experienced fear and the feeling of aloneness that came with the darkness in the vast, unfamiliar, unsettled land of the western United States.

When the railroads moved west to Texas and beyond, the cowboys no longer used the Chisholm Trail. They had to find other trails and face other dangers. Today, most of the land along the Chisholm Trail is used for farming.

Some Other Books To Read

Big Book of Cowboys by Sydney E. Fletcher. Published by Grosset and Dunlap, Inc., New York, 1950.

Trails West and Men Who Made Them by Edith Dorian. Published by Whittlesey House Publications, New York, 1955.

Cowboys and Cattle Country by Don Ward. Published by American Heritage Publishing Co., Inc., New York, 1962.

Arizona Cowboy by Frederic Remington

The Daring One-Armed Major

By Anne Merriman Peck

"I don't aim to get drowned in this canyon," growled Dunn.

The other men stared at him in dismay. Dunn was a trapper with lots of experience in wilderness country. If he was afraid, they were really in danger!

"I've never seen such waterfalls," Howland spoke up. "The whole river drops about twenty feet over the rocks. Then there are more falls and more rapids. You can't even see the river beyond the falls."

"Men, we set out to explore the Colorado canyons, all the way to the end," the one-armed major said. "Come now, don't let bad waterfalls scare you. We've had some narrow escapes before on this trip. Maybe this will be our last battle with the river."

The other men were too tired and discouraged to speak. They were trapped between the huge black walls of the canyon that towered several hundred feet above their heads. The river rushed between the cliffs with the speed of an express train. The roar of the rushing water echoed from wall to wall.

For three months these men had struggled through miles and miles of canyons. They had fought the river at its worst in the great gorges now called the Grand Canyon. Their boats had been overturned, beaten on rocks, and nearly smashed. Many times they had barely

escaped drowning. Now, when they listened to the terrifying roar of water ahead, their courage gave out.

"Major," shouted Howland above the noise of the water. "We'll never live through those falls. The boats will be smashed. We'll have to get out of the canyon some other way."

He turned and pointed to the towering walls, "There are some breaks and ridges in the cliffs. We could climb there and try to reach the top. It's not so dangerous as the river."

The major stood up and smiled at his comrades. The very sight of him gave them courage. This man had brought them through many tight spots, and they trusted him.

"Sure we're all tired and hungry," he

said. "There isn't much food left. But we have come through some mighty rough water. And we're still alive. I figure we're almost through the canyons. How can we give up now? I'm going on. I hope you will come with me!"

The major turned and walked along the shore while the other men argued among themselves.

"Look here, we can't desert the major," said Bradley, a young man who had been with the major in the army. "He's brought us through the worst of scrapes. Even though he has only one arm, he always takes on the hardest jobs himself."

"But we'll die if we take the boats over those falls," argued Howland. "Our only chance is to climb the cliffs and get out of this canyon."

Howland's brother agreed.

"I'll stick with the major," Bradley said.

"Count me in on that. I'm going all the way with the major," one of the other men said.

"Well, I'm going with the Howlands," Dunn said. "I'm not going to take a chance on those falls."

The other men decided to stay with the major.

When the major returned, Howland spoke first. "It's hopeless, major. We'll never get out of here alive. I'm leaving."

"Is that the decision of the group?" asked the major quietly.

The Howland brothers and Dunn nodded.

Bradley spoke for the others. "Major, the rest of us will stick it out with you to the end."

They decided to separate, but there was sadness in their hearts. They felt that they might never see each other again.

In the morning the Howland brothers and Dunn said good-by to their companions. They started the climb, from boulder to ledge, up the face of the canyon wall.

The other men turned to the boats. With their companions gone there were not enough men to handle three boats, so one boat was left behind.

"Let's go, men!" commanded the major. "No sense putting it off any longer."

As soon as the boats hit the swift current, they were swept downstream until the men steered them to a strip of shore near the falls. The waves breaking over rocks, the clouds of spray, and the thunder of water as the river rushed over the brink of the falls brought fear to every heart.

The major planned to launch one boat with a long, strong
rope tied to it. They would try to hold back the speed of the
boat by hanging on to the rope with all their strength, while
they clung to boulders on the shore. They would try this boat
over the falls first.

"Major, let me go with the boat," Bradley volunteered. "If the
rope breaks, we'll lose the boat unless there's someone to steer it
out of the rapids."

Before the major could answer, Bradley stepped into the boat
and pushed it out from shore. The waves seized it, tossed it back
against the cliffs, tossed it out again into the river, and dashed
it against rocks. The men held tight to the rope, but the pull of
the speeding boat was too powerful. The rope slipped from their
hands!

Horrified, they saw the boat go sweeping over the brink of the
falls. It disappeared in the waves and spray. What would hap-

pen to Bradley? Would he be crushed to death on the rocks?

At last, the anxious watchers saw Bradley tossing in the rapids below the falls. The boat was speeding ahead of him. While they watched, Bradley went under, then came to the surface again and fought the waves. He managed to reach the overturned boat and cling to it while he pushed it, bit by bit, out of the swift current to a cove of quiet water. Then he climbed into the boat and waved to his companions. But he was still in danger of being swept into a whirlpool.

"Come on, men, he's still in trouble," the major shouted. "We've got to get to him."

The major sent two men scampering over the cliffs.

The rest of the men climbed into the other boat and shoved it away from shore. At once they were sped toward the falls. Over the brink they went! They were thrown out of the boat. Down, down they sank, under torrents of water. Gasping for breath,

they struggled to the surface. Powerful waves swept over them, sucked them under, and rolled them over and over.

The men fought for their lives among the cruel rocks and smothering water. They swam when they could as the water swept them on and on. When the waves became less furious, they struggled ahead until they caught the boat. Slowly, they pushed it into the cove where Bradley was waiting on the shore, shouting and waving his arms. With Bradley's help, the battered men crawled out of the water. Soon the two who had gone over the cliffs joined them.

These tough men were not ashamed to hug each other. They were so glad to be alive! The major shook the water out of his hair and eyes like a wet dog.

"We're here, men, alive and safe," he gasped. "We've done it—we are the first men to come through the Colorado River canyons!"

The one-armed major in this story was John Wesley Powell. Major Powell and his companions made the first journey through the hundreds of miles of Colorado River canyons in 1869. The brave adventurers continued downstream after they conquered the falls until they came to a settlement. There they were welcomed heartily. No one had expected to see them alive. The three men who had left the party to climb the canyon wall reached the top, but had soon been killed by Indians.

Nowadays, skilled rivermen with special boats take parties through some of the Colorado canyons.

Some Other Books To Read

First Through the Grand Canyon by Steve Frazer. Published by John C. Winston Co., Philadelphia, 1960.

Down the Colorado with Major Powell by James Ramsey Ullman. Published by Houghton Mifflin Co., Boston, 1960.

Major John Wesley Powell

THE TWENTY-EIGHTH HOLDUP

"Hey, Mr. McConnell, Mr. McConnell!" Jimmy shouted as he ran toward the Wells, Fargo & Company office.

Mr. McConnell stepped out of the passenger compartment of the stagecoach when he heard Jimmy's shouts.

"What can I do for you, Jimmy?"

"Can I ride with you as far as Copperopolis?" Jimmy asked. "Ma says it's all right if you will let me."

"Sure, Jimmy. Glad to have company. I'm just about ready to leave."

"What were you doing in the passenger compartment?" Jimmy asked.

By Phyllis W. Heald

Mr. McConnell looked around to make sure nobody was listening. "Black Bart, the bandit, has been robbing the Wells, Fargo & Company stagecoaches around this area. I am carrying a shipment of gold, and since there aren't any passengers today, I am hiding the gold inside the coach. I was just strapping the box to the floor."

Mr. McConnell mounted to the driver's seat and turned to Jimmy. "Go around the other side and climb aboard. Then we'll be off."

Jimmy scrambled up to the seat using the spokes of the big wheel for a ladder. Carefully he placed his shotgun across his knees just as he had seen the men of Wells, Fargo & Company do.

Mr. McConnell picked up the reins. "Well, Jimmy, I see you brought your gun along. How about being my shotgun rider till we reach Copperopolis?"

"Sure, Mr. McConnell," Jimmy agreed quickly. He knew that drivers for Wells, Fargo & Company never carried guns themselves. The bandits knew this too and seldom shot a driver. But sometimes another man would ride along with a driver to help guard a valuable shipment. This was known as "riding shotgun."

"That will be great. And I'll keep a sharp lookout for Black Bart," Jimmy said.

Mr. McConnell looked ahead to be sure the way was clear. "Git up! Hi Yi! Get along! Yip-Yip!" he yelled.

The horses started off at a fast trot. Mr. McConnell called through the noise of the snorting horses, the cracking whip, and the creaking wheels, "Hang on tight, Jimmy. Your feet don't touch the floor, and you might bounce out."

Jimmy clutched the seat with one hand and clung to his shotgun with the other.

As soon as they were clear of town, the horses settled down to an even pace. It was a beautiful November morning. The scrub oak trees that lined the road were turning red. And the gently rolling hills beyond, all covered with tall yellow grass, looked like a carpet of gold.

Mr. McConnell took his gaze from the road for a quick glance at Jimmy's lap. "That looks like a new shotgun you have there."

"Pa gave it to me for my birthday. Isn't it a beauty?" Jimmy held it out so the driver could get a better look. "Pa thinks I'm old enough to start shooting turkey and small game for food. I'm going to practice shooting so when I grow up I can be a stagecoach messenger or a detective."

"We sure could use a good detective to catch Black Bart," Mr. McConnell said.

"Do you think Black Bart will ever be caught?"

"I hope so," Mr. McConnell answered. "Black Bart has robbed Wells, Fargo & Company twenty-seven times in the last eight years, and the company has had to repay all the stolen money."

"But how do you know that it was Black Bart who pulled all those robberies?"

"Black Bart always works the same way, Jimmy. He wears a long, light-colored overcoat and covers his head with a white flour sack that has openings for his eyes. He wears a derby hat. He has a deep voice, and he is always very polite. He never robs the passengers. But the thing that clinches the matter is that Black Bart always leaves a poem behind. And he always signs his poems the same way—'Black Bart, the PO 8!'"

Ahead, through the dust, Jimmy could see the gentle rise of a hill. He knew that Mr. McConnell would slow the horses to a walk when they reached the hill.

Jimmy had an idea.

"Say, can I get out and look for rabbits? I'll come along and meet you on top of the hill."

"Sure." Mr. McConnell pulled the team to a halt and let Jimmy climb down. "No rush, Jimmy. I'll wait on top of the hill and give the horses a rest."

Jimmy cut across the road through the trees to the clear grassland beyond. He stood quietly for a moment, watching. Suddenly a rabbit appeared on a nearby rock. He aimed and shot three times. But the rabbit ran away.

"Gosh," Jimmy said aloud. "I need practice all right."

Instead of hunting any more, he tried hitting a rock for a while. Not too proud of his shooting, he started on the run to catch up with the stagecoach.

When Jimmy came through the trees, he saw a strange sight. There was Mr. McConnell holding the horses quiet. But where was the stagecoach?

Jimmy walked over to Mr. McConnell.

"Shhh!" Mr. McConnell urged. "Black Bart's got the coach on the other side of the hill. He's taking the gold."

"What can we do?" Jimmy asked. "How can we stop him? I've got my shotgun."

"Come on," whispered Mr. McConnell. "Follow me! Let's see if we can get the draw on him."

They edged their way up the hill. They reached the top just in time to see the bandit straighten up and start backing out of the stagecoach. The bandit wore a light coat, with a white flour sack and a derby hat on his head. It was Black Bart, all right!

"Jimmy! Get behind him with your gun, while I take his gun and tie him up," Mr. McConnell said.

Quickly, Jimmy ran forward and pushed the muzzle of his shotgun into the bandit's back.

"Stick 'em up!" he shouted as fiercely as he could.

The bandit's hands shot into the air. He dropped his gun. Without a word, he started walking toward Mr. McConnell while Jimmy followed right behind with the gun still in the bandit's back.

"Looks like you've got me this time," the bandit said in his deep polite voice. But suddenly he made a dive into the bushes at the side of the road.

Taken completely by surprise, Jimmy hesitated a second.

Mr. McConnell ran toward him. "Give me the gun, Jimmy. You watch the horses," he said.

He grabbed Jimmy's shotgun, fired three times, and disappeared into the bushes after the bandit.

Jimmy gathered up the reins and looked anxiously in the direction both men had gone.

There wasn't a sound on the top of the hill. A buzzard circled in the sky and then dropped out of sight.

Jimmy looked toward the coach. He wondered if he dared leave the horses, and go after Mr. McConnell.

Just then he heard footsteps. He swung around to see Mr. McConnell step out on the road. His face was red. He looked hot and was breathing hard.

"He got away," Mr. McConnell said. "But I think I might have wounded him."

"Gee, I'm sorry he got away. But I'm sure glad you're all right." Jimmy sighed with relief.

"Thanks, Jimmy," Mr. McConnell said. "You were quite a help to me, you know."

"Well, gosh, I *had* to do something! I'm your shotgun rider!"

"That's right, son. And you're one of the best I ever had. You saved the gold shipment," Mr. McConnell said. He handed the rifle back to Jimmy. "Come on now, let's hitch this team and get along to Copperopolis."

Reason McConnell, the driver in this story, was one of the daring men of Wells, Fargo & Company who risked their lives to protect the shipments they carried in their stagecoaches. And young Jimmy, whose full name was James Rolleri, was like most of the boys of his time. He admired the men of Wells, Fargo & Company and wanted to be one himself when he became old enough.

Wells, Fargo & Company was an express organization that carried passengers, freight, and mail. The company specialized in carrying shipments of gold and silver across the American West. One of the dangers that the men had to face were bandits like Black Bart. After the Central-Union Pacific railroad was completed in 1869, shipments could be more safely sent by railroad, and Wells, Fargo & Company lost much of its business. In 1918, Wells, Fargo & Company merged with the American Railway Express Company.

This incident took place in California about one hundred years ago. A few weeks later, Black Bart was finally captured by a Wells, Fargo & Company detective.

Some Other Books To Read

Wells Fargo by Ralph Moody. Published by Houghton Mifflin Co., Boston, 1961.

William Fargo, Young Mail Carrier by Katherine E. Wilke. Published by The Bobbs-Merrill Company, Inc., Indianapolis, 1962.

AN EXCITING ESCAPE

By Charles M. Block

The young Englishman crouched in the shadows of the prison wall. He could hear the footsteps of the guards as they passed outside the wall. He had to wait for the exact moment when both sentries were out of sight. He waited, listening to the footsteps fading into the distance.

As he waited, he wondered. Why should he want to escape? After all, he wasn't a soldier. He had no regiment to return to. He was a reporter writing about this war for a London newspaper. He had been captured trying to save some English soldiers. Now, after three weeks, he realized that prison life wasn't so bad. Why bother risking his neck when he could spend the rest of the war safely behind these prison walls?

Why indeed, he thought.

But he knew the answer. The answer was that he had to be free. He couldn't stay in prison, no matter how safe it might be. Above all else, he must have his freedom!

He listened until he was sure the sentries were out of sight. Now was the time.

In an instant he was up and over the wall.

Then he was hiding in a bush on the other side. But freedom was still three hundred miles away. He had to get to the ocean before he would be truly free.

There was little time to lose before his escape would be discovered. Instead of waiting in his hiding place and taking the chance of being discovered, he slipped out of the bush and wandered into the streets of the enemy town, moving along with the crowd. So far, so good!

As he walked, a plan began to take shape in his mind. He knew that by morning his escape would have been discovered, and he would be a hunted man. By then he had to be as far away from the prison camp as possible. When he reached the other side of town, he came to a railroad track. Ah! That was it! This railroad ran toward the ocean. To him the ocean meant freedom.

Listening carefully, he heard the sound of a train approaching.

He crossed the tracks and kept hidden until the train came rattling by. Then he ran alongside the train, leaped, and clung desperately to the side of an open-topped freight car. His luck was still good. No one had seen him. He pulled himself up and over into the darkness of the car. The freight car was loaded with empty coalsacks. He wiggled down among the sacks, coughing from the coal dust, trying to make himself as comfortable as possible. And as the train rumbled on through the night, he slept.

It was still dark in the car when he awoke. He looked outside. The sky was sprinkled with stars. In the east, he could see the first traces of the gray dawn climbing into the blackness of the night sky. He had to be off the train before daylight. So, hoping his luck would not fail him now, he swung himself outside the car, and sprang from the speeding train. He rolled into a ditch. He got up bruised, but he wasn't hurt badly.

The air was heavy with dampness. Beads of perspiration popped out on his brow. The ground was wet and swampy. He found it hard to lift his boots out of the mud. The sun was beginning to rise, and he moved in the direction of the rising sun. He knew that was east, the way to the ocean and freedom.

The sky was clear. Not a cloud could be seen anywhere. It would be dangerous to travel by day because he might be seen by enemy soldiers. So he took shelter in some nearby woods to wait until nightfall when he could move without being spotted.

As the sun moved higher in the sky, he became hotter. Sweat rolled down his forehead into his eyes and mouth. His clothing, already damp from perspiration, stuck to his body.

He had had nothing to eat but chocolate since the night before. How thirsty he was! But he dared not drink the swamp water, because it might be poisonous. The day wore on. He grew weak, and his mouth became dry. Still the heat beat down on him.

All at once he was aware of someone, or something, watching him. He whirled around to see a large bird perched on a tree nearby, eying him curiously. It was a vulture!

"He'd like me for dinner," the young Englishman thought with

a shudder.

"You'll not have me tonight, vulture," he said aloud. Then he was annoyed with himself for speaking and taking the chance of being overheard by the enemy.

For the rest of the day, he and the vulture watched each other silently.

When at last the sun set, the coolness of night refreshed his weary body. He left the shelter of the woods and started, once again, on his journey. But as the night became blacker, the coolness turned to an icy cold. A chill crept through him.

How much longer can I go on, he wondered.

He moved slowly, keeping clear of roads, trying to stay close to whatever cover he could find. Many times he spotted enemy soldiers and had to stay hidden until they passed. He trudged through swamps and bogs and through thickets of tall, tangled grass.

He got weaker, but stumbled onward, no longer sure where he was going. He knew only that he must keep moving. Several times he fell into the swampy slime, but something inside him made him struggle to his feet again and go on with his journey.

Then he saw some lights ahead of him. Shivering, he moved toward the town. Perhaps here he might find some food and a place to rest without being caught.

What chance have I now, he thought. Here I am deep in enemy territory and probably without a friend for miles around.

He stumbled into the town. Then the weakness overtook him. Everything began to spin around. He fell.

Suddenly, he heard a voice calling softly to him from the shadows of a nearby house. "Over here!" the voice whispered. "Come here quickly!"

He crawled over to the spot where he had heard the voice. He saw a stranger crouched in the shadows.

"Speak quietly," the stranger said. "There are soldiers all around. I know who you are. You are that newspaper chap who escaped from prison."

"Who are you?" the young Englishman asked.

"My name is John Howard," the stranger replied. "I am an Englishman, too. In fact, I am the only one for miles around. It is lucky that it was I who found you. Soldiers have been searching for you since morning."

Tired, ragged, and dirty, the young English newspaperman stood up. "I'd better leave," he said. "If they find me with you, you'll be shot for trying to help me."

"Don't try it," John Howard ordered. "I know a place where you can hide. When you are well enough to move on, I'll help you get away."

John Howard took the young Englishman to an old mine pit, and there, below ground, the young man took refuge. Howard brought some food and water to him, and he was able to sleep. When he wasn't sleeping, he read some old books Howard had given him, by the flickering light of a candle. His only visitors were big rats that watched his every move through glaring pink eyes. Their monsterlike shadows danced along the walls of the mine in the candlelight. But even with these sinister companions,

the young Englishman knew he was safer in the darkness of this mine than he would be anywhere else. Above ground, the enemy soldiers were still searching for him.

On the morning of the third day, he awoke feeling much stronger. He had a long way to go in his dash to freedom, and he was eager to move on. He hoped John Howard would come for him soon.

Suddenly he heard footsteps approaching. He sat straight up. Had the enemy discovered where he was hiding?

Quickly he snuffed out the candle and crept into the darkest corner of the mine. He snatched up a board to use as a weapon. As the footsteps came closer, he raised the board above his head with both hands, ready to bring it crashing down on the head of the intruder.

Then he heard a voice calling his name. It was the voice of John Howard.

He breathed a sigh of relief. He dropped the board to the ground and came out to greet his friend.

John Howard said, "Listen carefully. I've arranged for your escape. Tonight, after dark, we're going to smuggle you onto a train headed for the ocean. Some men on the train will help you. There'll be an empty space among some bales of wool on one of the freight cars. You'll hide there. I'll come for you when it gets dark."

That night the young Englishman and John Howard crept quietly through the shadows to the railroad tracks. The train was waiting. When they were sure no one was looking, they quickly shook hands and said good-by to each other.

The young newspaperman slipped aboard the train and crawled in among the bales of wool. Then, the men who had promised to help him loaded more bales around him to keep him hidden. The train jolted and started to chug along the tracks, faster and faster. At last he was headed toward the ocean on the last leg of his journey.

But he was not free yet. Each time the train stopped, he wondered if enemy soldiers would climb on board to search for him.

Several times he caught himself dozing off. The bales of wool on which he lay were soft and comfortable. But he was afraid to sleep because he wanted to be alert to everything that happened.

He tried to stay awake, but he was still weak. And the rocking motion of the train made it all the more difficult for him to stay awake. Try as he might, he couldn't keep his eyes open. He fell into a deep sleep.

Then, in his sleep he heard voices—they spoke the enemy language! He awoke with a start. Had he been discovered? He took out the pistol John Howard had given him to use in case of emergency. Now he was wide awake. He waited, listening. The voices came closer. They were right outside his hiding place. He cocked his pistol.

But slowly the voices drifted away, and after a few minutes, the train started to move.

Again the rocking of the train made him drowsy, and though he tried to keep from falling asleep, he couldn't.

When he awoke again, it was daylight. He peered out of his hiding place to see where he was.

For the first time in days, a smile crossed his face. There in the distance, he could see the blue waters of the ocean. He was almost free.

At last the train rumbled across the frontier into friendly country. Delirious with joy, the young Englishman raised his pistol and began firing into the air.

He had escaped. He had made it. He was free!

Sir Winston Churchill giving his famous "V for Victory" salute

This exciting escape took place more than sixty years ago. It happened in South Africa during the Boer War, when the young man was not yet twenty-five years of age.

After he returned to London, the young newspaper reporter became a member of Parliament, the lawmaking body of Great Britain. His name, Winston Churchill, became known throughout the world. This famous writer, painter, and statesman became Prime Minister of Great Britain during World War II. It was he who led his country to victory. His faith and belief in the triumph of freedom over the enemies of freedom was well expressed in the symbol he used to inspire the British people: V for Victory.

Some Other Books To Read

Life of Winston Churchill by Leonard Wibberley. Published by Farrar, Straus, and Cudahy, Inc., New York, 1956.

Story of Winston Churchill by Alida Sims Malkus. Published by Grosset and Dunlap, Inc., New York, 1957.

THE WRONG ANGLE

"How much longer, mom?" Jay asked.

"Oh, about twenty minutes, I guess," his mother answered. "It will all be over soon."

according to a story
by Rene Carpenter

357

Jay dropped to the floor and sprawled out on his stomach with his legs straight out behind him. The points of his elbows dug into the rug and he cupped his chin in his hands. He stared at the television screen. The TV announcer's voice droned on and on telling about the space flight that was now nearly completed.

Jay listened to the voice without paying attention. He was thinking about the man who was in the space capsule that was orbiting the earth. That man was his dad.

Jay looked around the room. His mother's eyes were glued to the screen. She seemed to have forgotten that there was anyone else in the room with her. Jay's big brother Scotty was sitting on a footstool next to his mother. Scotty was restless. He kept fidgeting. Jay's two little sisters, Candy and Krissie, seemed bored. Candy was half asleep, almost falling off her footstool. Krissie was staring at the wall above the TV set. Her eyes were opened wide and her mouth drooped as if she were off in some daydream world. Her legs dangled over the edge of her bamboo chair and swung slowly back and forth.

The room was quiet except for the sounds coming from the TV set.

Jay thought about his dad, the greatest guy in the whole world. He knew that soon his dad would be a hero like George Washington and Abraham Lincoln. But his dad was a real person. The other heroes were just people you read about in books and whose pictures hung on the walls in school. Jay wondered if Abe Lincoln and George Washington and all the other heroes he had ever heard about were regular guys like his dad.

Much of the excitement and eagerness they had all felt that morning had passed. Now there was not much to do but to watch and wait as the hours crawled by. Jay thought back to early that morning, when the rocket carrying his father had blasted off from Cape Canaveral. It had been the most thrilling

moment of Jay's life. Shortly before blastoff his father had phoned from the capsule to tell them of the preparations, as the sounds of the booster below him carried through over the telephone. After the phone call the family had returned to the TV set as the countdown neared its end.

At the count of zero they had watched the huge rocket ship hang suspended over the launching pad and then start to rise slowly into the air. In a flash they all raced outside the beachhouse to watch the rocket, which was only a few miles away, lift out of the ground fog and soar up and up into the sky. Then they had rushed back into the house again to watch the rocket being tracked on a special telescope lens until it disappeared from the TV screen.

Jay had been more excited than he had ever been before. For a long while he had listened to all the reports that came in. He could even hear his father's voice, although it was a faraway voice, punctuated with static, that didn't sound like his father at all.

Their father had given both boys a copy of his flight plan so they would be able to know what he was doing throughout the flight. He would be making close to forty experiments and observations, and the family was listening eagerly for the report of each. Some of the things he would do would be to photograph the colors of sunrise and sunset, and to launch a balloon from the capsule to see whether it would drag behind or follow alongside the capsule. And with *his* copy of the flight plan Jay could pretend that he, himself, was in the capsule making the experiments. He imagined himself trying to eat solid foods in the weightlessness of space and watching how a flask of liquid would react where there was no up or down. Jay pictured himself looking out at the earth's cloud formations from outer space. And he pretended that it was he who was looking for the strange particles of light which another astronaut, Colonel Glenn, had described as luminescent fireflies.

Jay listened closely to the reports as they came in. Sometimes the TV announcer gave the information, and sometimes Jay could hear his father's voice making the reports. As the morning wore on, Jay learned that the balloon experiment had been spoiled when the balloon had only filled up part way. He laughed when he found out that the solid food had crumbled and floated around the capsule when his dad had tried to eat. And then Jay discovered that his dad had spotted the strange particles of light, which he described as looking like snowflakes, by rapping the side of the capsule and dislodging frostlike flakes.

The news of these and the other experiments had held Jay's attention for much of the morning. But after awhile the children had grown restless. Jay and Scotty had started to horse around by wrestling and rolling across the floor. But their mother had stopped them. Instead, she had them do push-ups. And later she had fed them lunch, made them do the dishes, and sent them out to swim on the beach.

Now the morning was gone and soon their father would be coming back down to earth.

Jay wished the flight would end. Not that he was worried, but still and all he knew he would feel better when it was all over.

He glanced around the room again. No one had moved. They were all in the same places as when he had looked before.

A word the TV announcer said broke through Jay's thoughts. The word was "re-entry." Jay saw his mother stiffen for just an instant. Her eyes never left the screen. Her hand glided slowly up to her mouth and without realizing it, she began to nibble on the tip of her finger.

Re-entry. Jay knew that could be one of the most dangerous parts of the flight. But Jay was sure his dad could handle it. He remembered that the capsule was slowed down with retrorockets so that it could leave its orbit and return to earth.

Suddenly Jay had to get up. He sprang to his feet and ran straight into Scotty's footstool.

"I'm a retrorocket!" he shouted.

That was all Scotty needed. He was restless anyway.

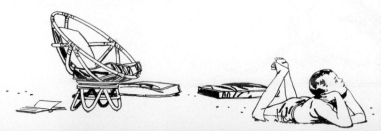

Soon both boys were racing around the room bumping into things and yelling, "I'm a retrorocket! I'm a retrorocket!"

The girls started to giggle and run after them.

But their mother was having none of that. She herded them back to their places in front of the TV set.

All four children were still giggling when the announcer reported that radio contact with the space capsule had been lost.

Jay and Scotty became suddenly silent. The girls kept laughing for a few seconds until they realized that their brothers had stopped. Then they were quiet too.

But Jay wasn't scared. He knew that this was supposed to happen during the re-entry and that the people at Cape Canaveral should be in touch with his dad again in about four or five minutes.

Then another report came through, that the officials at Cape Canaveral were afraid the capsule might be coming in at a bad angle and would not land where it was supposed to.

Jay sat down in one of the bamboo chairs in front of the set. Now he *was* scared a little. What if the angle really was bad? What if it got too hot inside the space capsule? What if . . . ?

Jay stopped himself in the middle of this last thought. He was perspiring as if he were up there in the capsule with his father. But there was nothing to worry about. His dad had said so.

Then Jay realized that more than five minutes had passed. The people at Cape Canaveral were not in touch with his father yet. Why? Was something *really* wrong?

He glanced at his mother. She was sitting on the floor staring at the screen. Her mouth was opened slightly. Her fingers kept moving back and forth across her throat. He could see that she was worried.

Then the announcer said that the space capsule was not being picked up on radar.

Jay slumped down in his chair and his chin sank down on his chest. Scotty tried to make a joke, but nobody laughed Even little Candy felt everyone's fears and she climbed on her mother's lap.

Jay had to admit that he was scared now. He thought of all

the things he and his dad had done together, all the places they had been to. Then he remembered something that had happened just a few days before. Scotty had brought home a sick bird that he had found in the woods. The boys were going to nurse it back to health and let it go when it was able to fly again. But the bird had died.

Jay glanced at his mother. Her expression hadn't changed. She was still sitting in exactly the same spot. She said matter-of-factly, "I know he's down now, but the capsule is out of tracking range."

Jay was worried, but at the same time, he was thinking about how he and his Dad would discuss the whole thing later.

The announcer said that rescue teams were searching the spot in the Atlantic Ocean where the capsule should have come down.

Please find him, Jay thought. He could picture the destroyers, planes, and helicopters searching the ocean for a tiny speck that might be his father. He could picture his father all alone on a life raft, scanning the empty skies for some sign of help.

How will they ever find him? Jay found himself wondering, even as he was remembering his father telling him about all the ways that would be used to locate him.

Suddenly, Jay became aware of loud noises going on all around him. Scotty was shouting something at him, but Jay couldn't quite make out the words. Then his mind cleared.

". . . spotted!" Scotty was yelling. "They've spotted him in the Atlantic Ocean. He's safe!"

Jay leaped from his chair and joined in the laughing and shouting. He could hardly wait to see his dad to ask him more about those fireflies, or snowflakes, or whatever they were.

The man who made the space flight in this story was Malcolm Scott Carpenter who, on May 24, 1962, became the fourth United States astronaut to be launched into space, and the second American to orbit the earth.

Like Scott Carpenter, each of the original seven astronauts had been well trained to meet any emergencies that might occur in flight. Each astronaut had served his country as a member of the U.S. Armed Forces.

Like Scott Carpenter's family, the families of each of the astronauts were prepared to watch and wait, and to accept whatever glories or tragedies they had to face.

Rene Carpenter, the author of this story, is the mother of Jay, and the wife of Scott Carpenter.

Here are the names of the first seven U.S. astronauts:

Malcolm Scott Carpenter, U.S. Navy
Leroy G. Cooper, Jr., U.S. Air Force
John H. Glenn, Jr., U.S. Marine Corps
Virgil I. Grissom, U.S. Air Force
Walter M. Schirra, Jr., U.S. Navy
Alan B. Shepard, Jr., U.S. Navy
Donald K. Slayton, U.S. Air Force

Some Other Books To Read

Space Pilots by Willy Ley. Published by Golden Press, Inc., New York, 1957.

A Book of Moon Rockets for You by Franklyn M. Bradley. Published by The Crowell-Collier Publishing Co., New York, 1959.

Rockets Through Space; the Story of Man's Preparations to Explore the Universe by Lester Del Rey. Published by Holt, Rinehart and Winston, Inc., New York, 1960.

What Does An Astronaut Do? by Robert Wells. Published by Dodd, Mead and Co., New York, 1961.

Malcolm Scott Carpenter

Blastoff

Recovery

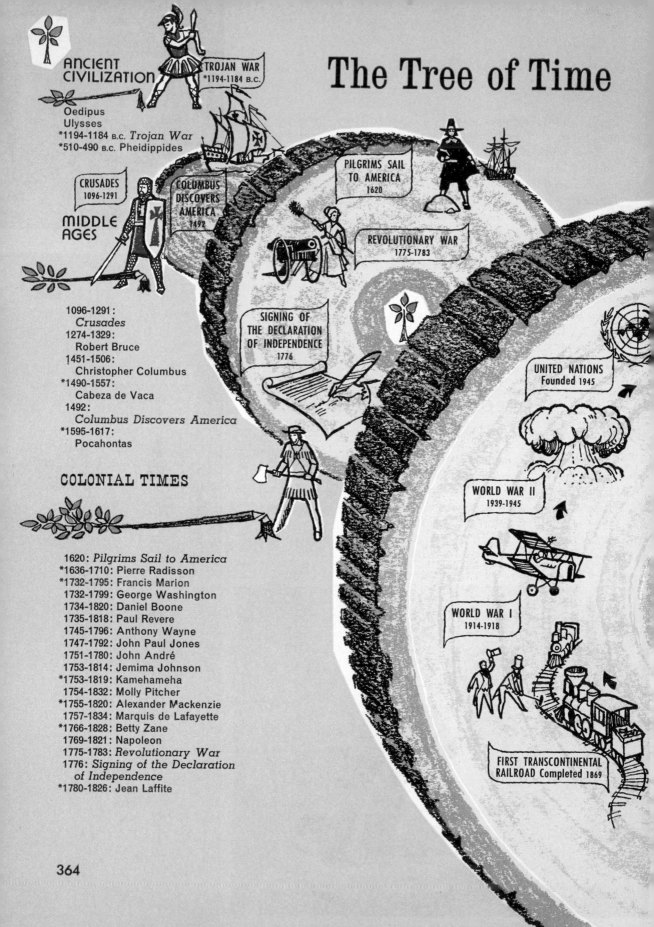

The Tree of Time

ANCIENT CIVILIZATION

TROJAN WAR
*1194-1184 B.C.

Oedipus
Ulysses
*1194-1184 B.C. Trojan War
*510-490 B.C. Pheidippides

CRUSADES
1096-1291

MIDDLE AGES

COLUMBUS DISCOVERS AMERICA 1492

1096-1291:
    Crusades
1274-1329:
    Robert Bruce
1451-1506:
    Christopher Columbus
*1490-1557:
    Cabeza de Vaca
1492:
    Columbus Discovers America
*1595-1617:
    Pocahontas

COLONIAL TIMES

1620: Pilgrims Sail to America
*1636-1710: Pierre Radisson
*1732-1795: Francis Marion
1732-1799: George Washington
1734-1820: Daniel Boone
1735-1818: Paul Revere
1745-1796: Anthony Wayne
1747-1792: John Paul Jones
1751-1780: John André
1753-1814: Jemima Johnson
*1753-1819: Kamehameha
1754-1832: Molly Pitcher
*1755-1820: Alexander Mackenzie
1757-1834: Marquis de Lafayette
*1766-1828: Betty Zane
1769-1821: Napoleon
1775-1783: Revolutionary War
1776: Signing of the Declaration
    of Independence
*1780-1826: Jean Laffite

PILGRIMS SAIL TO AMERICA 1620

REVOLUTIONARY WAR 1775-1783

SIGNING OF THE DECLARATION OF INDEPENDENCE 1776

UNITED NATIONS Founded 1945

WORLD WAR II 1939-1945

WORLD WAR I 1914-1918

FIRST TRANSCONTINENTAL RAILROAD Completed 1869

for PIONEERS and PATRIOTS

This volume begins in ancient Greece and ends at the present. The tree of time shows when the heroes of this volume lived in relation to one another and to the great events of history. The tree is shown here at four different stages of its growth—Ancient Civilization, Middle Ages, Colonial Times, and Modern Times. Can you recognize the people whose pictures are inside the tree?

FIRST MEN ORBIT EARTH
1961-1962

MODERN TIMES

FIRST TRIP ALONG
THE OREGON TRAIL
1830

MODERN TIMES

COLONIAL TIMES

MIDDLE AGES

ANCIENT CIVILIZATION

WELLS, FARGO & COMPANY
Founded 1852

PONY EXPRESS
1860-1861

CIVIL WAR
1861-1865

FIRST TRIP ALONG
THE CHISHOLM TRAIL
1866

1783-1830: Simón Bolívar
1786-1836: Davy Crockett
*1787-1812: Sacagawea
1793-1863: Sam Houston
1801-1870: David Farragut
1807-1870: Robert E. Lee
1807-1882:
   Giuseppe Garibaldi
1809-1868: Kit Carson
*1815-1874: Cochise
1824-1863:
   Stonewall Jackson
*1826-1862: J. J. Andrews
*1830: *First Trip Along
   the Oregon Trail*
1834-1902:
   John Wesley Powell
1844-1900: Belle Boyd
1846-1917:
   Buffalo Bill Cody
1852: *Wells, Fargo
   & Company
   Founded*
1860-1861: *Pony Express*
1861-1865: *Civil War*
1866: *First Trip Along
   the Chisholm Trail*
1869: *Completion of First
   Transcontinental
   Railroad*
1874-____:
   Winston Churchill
1914-1918: *World War I*
1925-____:
   Scott Carpenter
1939-1945: *World War II*
1945: *United Nations
   Founded*
1961-1962: *First Men
   Orbit Earth*
*Approximate Dates

365

Illustration
Acknowledgments

The publishers of CHILDCRAFT gratefully acknowledge the courtesy of the following artists, photographers, publishers, agencies, and corporations for illustrations in this volume. Page numbers refer to two-page spreads. The words "(*left*)," "(*center*)," "(*top*)," "(*bottom*)," and "(*right*)," indicate position on the spread. All illustrations are the exclusive property of the publishers of CHILDCRAFT unless names are marked with an asterisk (°).

8–17: Charles Harper
18–25: Alice and Martin Provensen
26–33: Mary Hauge; (*page 33*), print, Culver (°); photo, United Press Int. (°)
34–39: Kathleen Elgin; tartan courtesy William Anderson & Sons Ltd., Edinburgh
40–47: Jack Breslow—Promotional Arts, Inc.; photo (*page 40*) Ewing Galloway (°), painting (*page 46*), "Columbus Takes Possession of the New World," watercolor by Johann Rugendas, courtesy Joe and Emily Lowe Art Gallery Collection, Coral Gables, Florida (°)
48–55: Joseph Watson Little
56–63: Robert Glaubke; painting (*page 63*) "Pocahontas," British School, courtesy National Gallery of Art, Washington, D.C. (°)
64–71: Don Almquist
72–77: Vic Dowd
78–85: Seymour Fleishman
86–91: James M. Sessions
92–97: Ronald Osiecki—Stephens Biondi De Cicco Inc.; painting (*page 97*) "Marquis de Lafayette" by F. G. Casanova, courtesy of The New-York Historical Society, New York City (°)
98–105: Vic Dowd; painting (*page 101*) "Moll Pitcher at the Battle of Monmouth 1778," by John Ward Dunsmore, courtesy Sons of the Revolution Headquarters, Fraunces Tavern, New York City, color photo courtesy *American Heritage* Magazine (°)
106–111: George Suyeoka; portrait (*page 111*) by Edward Savage, courtesy of The New-York Historical Society, New York City (°)
112–117: Roy Andersen; sketch (*page 116*) Yale University Art Gallery, gift of Ebenezer Baldwin (°)
118–125: Everett McNear; photo (*page 125*) Gottscho-Schleisner (°)
126–135: Rod Ruth; photo (*page 135*) New York Public Library (°)
136–141: Francis Chase
142–149: William Moyers; photo (*page 149*) in the collection of The National Gallery of Canada, Ottawa (°)
150–157: Joseph Watson Little
158–167: Tak Murakami; (*page 166*) by permission of Dr. and Mrs. Ernest Harms, photo courtesy *Antiques* Magazine (°)
168–177: Walter Baumhofer
178–187: Charles Moser; photo (*page 187*) Bradley Smith (°)
188–195: Mary Horton; photos (*page 195*) "Cherokee Chief John Jolly," by George Catlin, courtesy Smithsonian Institution (°); "General Sam Houston at Battle of San Jacinto," as painted by S. Seymour Thomas, from Wide World (°)

196–203: photography by Vincent Maselli, art by Bob Ulm
204–211: Franz Altschuler; photo (*pages 204–205*) Robert Holland (°) (*page 211*) Alfa Studio
212–221: Denver Gillen; painting (*pages 220–221*) "The Battle of New Orleans," courtesy Yale University Art Gallery, Mabel Brady Garvan Collection (°)
222–229: Betty Leaffe Peterson; painting (*page 229*) "Bonaparte au Mont St. Bernard," by Jacques-Louis David, courtesy Museum of Versailles and the Trianons, France (°)
230–237: Seymour Fleishman; photos (*page 230*) Dwight C. Sturgis for *Christian Science Monitor* (°), (*page 237*) H. Armstrong Roberts (°)
238–245: Gurney Miller; photo (*page 245*) Ansel Adams (°)
246–253: Helen Prickett; fish illustration (*page 246–247*) Jack J. Kunz (°); photo (*page 253*) West Virginia Publicity Commission (°)
254–263: Walter Baumhofer; photo (*page 254*) San Antonio Chamber of Commerce (°), watercolor (*page 263*) by Anthony Lewis De Rose, courtesy of The New-York Historical Society, New York City (°)
264–273: Gurney Miller; photo (*page 273*) by Fred H. Ragsdale, Publix (°)
274–281: Richard Loehle
282–289: William Hollingshead; photo (*page 289*) Elliott L. Foy, courtesy Denver Public Library Western Collection (°)
290–297: Seymour Fleishman; photos (*page 294*) Alfred Gescheidt, (°) (*page 296*) The Mansell Collection, London (°)
298–305: Helen Prickett; photo (*page 298*) U.S. Forest Service (°)
306–313: Seymour Fleishman
314–319: Clark Bruorton
320–329: Ross Santee; pastel (*page 329*) "An Arizona Cowboy," from "Buckskins" series, by Frederic Remington, reproduced by permission Remington Art Memorial, Ogdensburg, New York (°)
330–337: Elizabeth Schon; photos (*page 331*) A. Y. Owen, courtesy *Life* Magazine, © 1956 Time Inc. (°), (*page 335*) Sperry Weaver (°), (*page 336*) David Muench (°), (*page 337*) courtesy William Culp Darrah (°)
338–345: Gordon Laite; photo (*page 345*) courtesy Wells Fargo Bank History Room, San Francisco (°)
346–355: David Cunningham; photo (*page 355*) United Press Int. (°)
356–363: art (*pages 356–357*) Art Magee, (*pages 358–361*) Richard Lowe; photos (*page 363*) National Aeronautics and Space Administration (°)
364–365: Tom Dunnington

Index to Volume 12

Use this index to find the authors, the major characters, and the subjects of the stories in this volume. The authors' names are in italics. To find the title of a story, look at the Table of Contents in the front of the book.

A general index to Volumes 1 through 13 appears in Volume 15.